CW00539404

THE THIRD BRIDGE

Jane Evans

APS Books
Yorkshire

APS Books,
The Stables, Field Lane,
Aberford,
West Yorkshire,
LS25 3AE

APS Books is a subsidiary of
the APS Publications imprint

www.andrewsparke.com

First published worldwide by APS Books 2022

PART 1

CHILDHOOD: THE NINETEEN FIFTIES AND SIXTIES

Chapter 1

Music: *'Que sera, sera'*; Doris Day (1956)

I was shivering, attempting to sleep when I saw a flickering light sweep through the loose opening of in our makeshift tent and disappear swiftly into the darkness. My best friends, Pearl Jones and Anna Klein were both asleep - we had talked for hours into the night - so my frantic scream, jerked them out of deep slumber. They reacted in terror. "What's the matter?" shrieked Anna, "What's happened?"

"My god, I've seen a ghost!"

"Oh, don't be silly, Sian", castigated Anna sharply, struggling to maintain her customary rational stance in spite of her fear. "What's the matter with you? Ghosts don't exist".

"Oh yes they do. I've just seen something really, really weird, a strange moving light. Listen, I know what I saw was a ghost. It couldn't be anything else. I saw a sort of thing' passing close to the tent and ...."

The three of us were rooted to the spot until Anna suddenly seized control and defiantly tore back the tent flap. She stuck her head out ready for battle but within seconds she collapsed into laughter, whilst Pearl and I stiffly held onto each other trembling with closed eyes.

"It's Bob Roberts on Black Bess. He's slumped over the horse drunk again and it's his flashlight causing all this mayhem. It's his flickering torch, definitely not a supernatural being!

"Are you absolutely sure?" I ventured hesitatingly, ashamed of my outburst. "Why would he come through this field?"

"Because it's *his* field, silly", said Anna impatiently and if he's that drunk, he leaves the steering to Bess, and this field is where she's usually tethered. Really Sian, how could you think Bob Roberts was a ghost?"

I felt embarrassed by my outburst in front of my friends. I had far too vivid an imagination for my own good - so my teachers were always telling my grandmother. Anna and Pearl were more emotionally balanced than I was, but both of them said that I was far more fun. My teachers were not impressed by my 'fun credentials' saying that I was the ringleader of a gang of three that needed to apply itself more rigorously to specific study if I wanted to pass the Eleven Plus or I would fail and end up at the local Secondary Modern school - known locally as *the Sin Bin*. The teachers agreed it would be a shame if I ended up with the dunces as I was 'quite bright.'

The three of us met at our village primary school and our friendships were bolstered by our mutual fascination with Enid Blyton's *Famous Five*. We exchanged books, camped in freezing rain in an irate farmer's field and convinced ourselves in the Blyton tradition that our head teacher was smuggling diamonds.

Pearl and I were the closest of buddies from the beginning but Anna Klein didn't really win her title as *a very special friend* until she had helped us steal apples from the bearded lady's garden. The bearded lady was a single woman called Frances Probert who had lived in her dilapidated cottage since we remembered.

She had thick white whiskers sprouting from her chin and was the victim of many spiteful children who shouted insults at her appearance across the garden wall. "Are you going to be Santa this Christmas, Frances? You won't need a false beard!".

Her house was rumoured to be filthy since her elderly father died but her garden was always well tended and she had the sweetest rosy apples in the village. One day, the bearded lady spotted us helping ourselves to her fruit. She let out a string of curses and immediately chased after us, whirling her walking stick like a club around her head but fortunately for us, she was short sighted and didn't recognise who we were. Panting with fear, we reached the exit to her garden and tumbled out into the road. A complaint about the trespass was later raised with our school but in true cowardly fashion we stayed silent when children were asked to confess to the apple crime and we all breathed a huge sigh of relief when finally, the subject of the stolen apples and the village policeman rescinded into the annals of time.

The idealised and greatly aspired to Grammar School was in the small local market town of Foistneth, eight miles away from the village where we children were raised and survived - in one dysfunctional way or another. Anna's parents were 'foreign' and her mother clung to the unreasonable belief that Anna would be struck down by pneumonia if she attempted an overnight stay in a tent. She was not allowed to camp for some years in spite of our repeated invitations, but eventually her father, the local G.P., relented because he wanted his daughter to have friends and join in with Welsh village life.

During our first year at Grammar School, Pearl's family moved to Foistneth as her father had purchased a café (named Wilf's Caff) near to the local bus station. The family sold pork pies and chips to lorry drivers and stewed tea and stale iced buns to passers-by with limited culinary choices in the town after 4 p.m.. Many customers took advantage of the 6 p.m. late closing of Wilf's Caff to shelter from the searing wind and rain while waiting for erratic buses to the rural Welsh villages. Nevertheless, there was a serious warning about Wilf's caff circulating at the time: 'If you want a quick meeting with the Divine and do not have the courage to end it yourself - consume a pork pie at Wilf Jones' caff' and then douse down a cup of stewed tea with a couple of stale iced buns. It will absolve you from any further pain of personal responsibility.'

Nevertheless, both Anna and I survived food poisoning, in spite of spending many weekends *at the caff* on the pretext of helping Pearl's parents. Anna's parents were Jewish and even though Mrs Klein did not keep a kosher home, she would have been horrified had she known her daughter was sampling Wilf's pork pies but Anna was too timid to refuse and there was rarely anything else for tea. I can still recall Anna's dilemma and her distress one particular evening when we were ravenous after playing outdoors all day and only pork sausages and ham and chips were on the menu.

What I ate was never an issue with my mother who not only couldn't cook but despised those who did.

"I can't imagine why those empty-headed women spend their lives poring over a stove", said my mother acerbically. This phrase was frequently repeated during the course of her life. Once when a child, I asked her whether she believed the stove was responsible for 'the empty heads' or whether 'intelligent heads' would have made any difference to her opinion of women who like cooking.

She responded with anger. "You think you're so clever, don't you?"

Any disagreement between us inevitably ended with my mother taking everything personally, getting angry and then weeping whilst dramatically proclaiming herself a victim.

I was devastated by Pearl's move to Foistneth and felt my very life was threatened when I learned she would no longer be supportively sitting next to me on the school bus. Some of the girls from the local Secondary Modern school were prone to picking on us and calling us nasty names. "Stuck ups!", they'd yell. "Who do you think you are? You're all so ugly you'll never get a boyfriend!"

We believed them but we also knew - even without parental remonstrations - that they envied us and we were the privileged few of a grossly unfair and punitive academic and social system.

I had only 'scraped' the Eleven Plus entrance exam to the Grammar School (a fact my mother, particularly when drunk, did not hesitate to remind me of) and the year before two girls with marks higher than my own had failed to gain entry. The boys' Grammar School had more places than the girls' and what determined any borderline cases like mine was the percentage pass mark of a particular examination year, rather than a specific score attained. Anna, I knew, would have passed whatever the percentage was in any one year in any millennium. Pearl, though by no means in the same category as Anna, had also done better than me.

So, there we were on a school bus with some nice kids and some really nasty characters with mega-chips on their shoulders whether socially derived or individually constructed. Safety was always in numbers so when Pearl left the bus I was deeply embarrassed about sitting on my own or next to Miss Doody, a stick thin severe-looking lady with an enormous black bun with astounding streaky lines of white hair drawn tightly to the nape of her scrawny neck. All the school bus kids giggled and mocked when Miss Doody, a ludicrously old-fashioned secretary at a reputable firm of solicitors in Foistneth, was mentioned. She sat primly on the bus, aptly balancing the Foistneth Chronicle against the faded strawberry coloured cloth of the back of the seat before her.

Miss Doody's expression was always tight-lipped and humourless. I often wondered how demoralising it must be for someone who had broken the law and in need of reassurance to be faced with such a stiff and expressionless at presence at the typewriter when they entered their solicitor's office for the first time. On reflection, this woman can only have been in her late thirties but she appeared really old to us and totally devoid of any sex appeal. Well, perhaps compared to Sandra Dee, our movie star heroine of the time, Miss Doody was devoid of any appeal whatsoever. One thing was certain, no one dared to pick on you if you sat next to Miss Doody. When I could I sat next to Anna but it was not always possible as she caught the bus at the busy stop before mine and almost every seat was taken by the time I got on. Grabbing a bus seat next to a friend or someone you could talk to was like playing Russian roulette.

Anna's parents were German Jews who had escaped the rise of Hitler and Nazi persecution. They both spoke excellent English but with accents that the rural Welsh had difficulty comprehending. Few of the villagers actually spoke Welsh in our agricultural area unlike the people of the South Wales mining valleys and Welsh was not, at that time, a compulsory subject at school. Anna feared the school children would tease her about her parents so she tried desperately hard at secondary school to keep them away from public functions, not an easy thing to do with parents like Anna's who were very committed to their daughter's education. But in spite of the teasing, anti-Semitism was not a burning issue at the Grammar School where one teacher was said to have a Jewish father and another had a great love for *Palestine and Jewish culture*. No, the labelling lurked outside school, particularly on the school bus. Reactivating memories of childhood and pondering over their significance, I cannot label what Anna experienced as 'anti-Semitism' because none of the worst offenders in our area knew what being Jewish meant. Instead, the tormentors were enacting the prejudices and biased views of their parents and the wider society by engaging in a cruel and vicious targeting difference - whether biological, social or cultural. Once a child on the school bus yelled: "Anna Klein - you killed our lord!"

"No, she didn't", shouted back a male voice from the back of the bus: "Bob Roberts' father killed Lord - he shattered his skull - the drunken bugger! My mother told me."

Few of us on the bus could remember the time when the village football team was called *The Lordies* or remember their mascot, a stray mongrel sheepdog adopted by a local farmer. It transpired that Bob Roberts' father, like his son after him, was not averse to a pint or two and one night he shot Lord, who was rummaging aggressively in his garden, believing the dog to be a burglar. Old Roberts ended up in court and would later claim fame in *The Foistneth Chronicle*. The football team subsequently changed its name to *The Robins* but this time for safety's sake, did not adopt a live mascot. Instead they acquired a large plastic robin on an adjustable pole. It had a bizarre gash for a beak that gave it a frightening expression that terrified young children. No one had ever seen a beak like that on a live robin!

So, due to the interpretation of village events, rather than biblical implications, Anna was never targeted on the issue again. Instead Anna's problem was a slightly large, angular nose which she was teased about mercilessly. Her quiet composure and modulated Welsh accent were interpreted as *stuck-up-ness* and an additional cause for mimicry and insults from the mainly under-achieving kids on the school bus.

In contrast, Pearl was spared the comments about 'stale pork pies walking out' of her father's shop and 'building an ice rink from the grease of the chips' discarded on the pavement outside, because she was rarely around to hear them. Having moved home she was consequently spared the taunts.

Anna and I continued on the school bus until we were sixteen but by then our tormentors had either left school, learned better manners, or become too interested in the opposite sex to spare many thoughts for our physical and social short comings.

Kids teased and insulted me because I came from one of the few families in the village that had divorced parents. I remember little about my father who had abandoned my mother and myself when I was eight. My maternal grandmother hadn't got a good word to say about him and she treated myself and my mother to long diatribes of how 'one should never marry below one's station'. My mother would burst into tears at this but I had difficulty comprehending how proximity to a station had anything to do with a good marriage. This anecdote has always amused me and brings fond memories of my determined and powerful grandmother - particularly when I travel by train. Within the swirling and vibrant mosaic of childhood memories, there were undoubtedly happy times, but etched on my personal experience is bleakness, sadness and self-doubt. My parents were often in conflict - whether overt or covert - and emotional discomfort was sucked into my childhood existence, as if by Dora Jones' new vacuum cleaner. I admit that I remember few rows between them but my inner feelings were always in turmoil, anxious and intense, waiting for the worst to crush and destroy our very existence. I was rarely wrong because things inevitably turned out badly for my mother and she cried a lot in her desperation for love and support. It was not uncommon for me to return from elementary school and find my mother weeping on the stairs over an unpaid bill or the latest misdemeanour committed by my absent father. When my mother started drinking she became even more tearful and depressed.

My grandmother and my mother were so unalike, both in character and appearance. My grandmother was tall, straight and slim with magnificent bone structure that many commented on, especially when looking at past photographs of her. My mother, on the other hand, was all of a dumpy 4 feet 10 inches. She had abundant black hair held back from her face by an Alice band. She was called Alice and her hairband gave her a sense of identity. My mother might even have been considered attractive if she had made more of an effort with makeup and self-care and showed more attention to her diet. She resembled my Welsh grandfather in appearance.

Elwyn Thomas was a couple of inches shorter than his wife, with curly black hair and a walrus moustache. But unlike my mother, he had a wonderful singing voice, a droll sense of humour and plenty of time for me. He was an educated man and used to be a schoolmaster at one of the elementary schools in a Swansea Valley mining village. My grandmother's family were English and my grandparents met at a performance of Verdi's Nabucco at Swansea Grand Theatre. My grandmother, then Geraldine Weston, was intended for a wealthy farmer in Malvern. She disappointed her parents by her marriage as they believed with her looks and keen intelligence she could have done better -as indeed she believed of her own daughter - my mother. But Geraldine married for what was then called 'love' and is now more aptly named 'sexual attraction'. Their marriage was never good due to their incompatibility of personality, diverse interests and eventually my grandfather's ill health and early retirement. This took place against the backdrop of the financial hardship and unemployment of the 1930s. When my mother was seven and her brother Theodore a small baby, they moved to a rural parish eight miles away from the market town of Foistneth. Through English contacts, my grandmother found work as a housekeeper to a local baronet and my grandfather tutored the baronet's children. They were also given one of the baronet's cottages in the village at a nominal rent.

Whenever my grandmother heard 'The chorus of the Hebrew slaves' on the radio, she would brusquely turn it off, regardless of who was listening. I was curious about why she did this and romantically assumed she did not want to be upset by memories of my grandfather and all he had meant to her in their young days. Instead, my mother said:

"I think it's more about regretting she fell for my father and missing out on the wealth and social position of that gentleman farmer in Malvern".

I never learned what became of my grandmother's family as she never spoke of them to any of us.

Chapter 2

Music: *'All I have to do is dream'*. The Everly Brothers, 1958

My grandfather enjoyed 'a tipple' behind my grandmother's back and was well versed at hiding whisky bottles and camouflaging the smell of alcohol on his breath. He was very aware of my mother's 'for medicinal purposes only' wine bottle. She told me many years later that her father used to talk to her with concern about her drinking but he didn't openly challenge or castigate her. He rightly believed that she was already getting her steady share of criticism from my grandmother.

My mother was rarely around to greet me on my return from school. She was in bed feigning illness with a bottle of sherry carefully hidden in the shabby green ottoman next to her double bed. Eventually we moved in with my grandmother as we could not afford to pay the rent on our gloomy little house. But I missed the house, particularly the sprawling apple-tree with its unusual, severed trunk in the shape of a goblin just outside my bedroom window. I was convinced fairies lived in the tree. When I wanted to escape the sadness and upheavals of everyday life, I would climb into the tree and pretend I was in Enid Blyton's 'Faraway Tree' a million light miles away. It was a secure and warm land of make-believe where I had control, away from the significant adults in my life with their conflicting versions of 'the truth'. In the Faraway Tree I felt calm and happy.

At my grandmother's, I shared a bedroom with my mother as my Uncle Theodore (my mother's younger brother) was still living at home and he occupied the third bedroom. I didn't like Uncle Theodore who was unattached, impatient and frequently rude to my mother when my grandmother wasn't around. Uncle Theodore worked in a bank and had to travel sixteen miles to work on a local bus each day. He felt so travel sick during the many years of a daily thirty-two-mile round trip that he lost his sense of humour - or at least this was my mother's perception of events. Uncle Theo was indeed humourless, especially when household bills were due to be paid and he smelled Sanatogen wine on my mother's breath. He used to take me aside and mumble into his brogues: "You don't want to be like your mother, do you?"

"Why, Uncle Theo?"

"No 'Why'. You don't want to be a liar and spend your money on booze like her, do you?"

His question made me uncomfortable, especially since my grandmother's neighbour kept telling me to be 'a wonderful woman like your mother'. At a very young age I experienced adults as unpredictable and they made me feel insecure and confused. I felt I never really knew the rules and if I once thought I had a grasp on some of them, they were crassly changed without any consultation so I felt a churning sense of anxiety and unease much of the time during my early childhood.

My grandmother was undoubtedly the best of my odd and unstable family but her verbal attacks on my mother made me angry and frightened of losing - I don't know what - perhaps the little safety I had. I was afraid that if I angered my grandmother, my mother and I would again be homeless.

My grandfather had a weak heart for many years due to rheumatic fever. He died during the first year I was at Grammar School. His sudden death was a great shock even though his health had been precarious for many years. We all knew he could leave us anytime, but I lived in dread of the day when this would happen. He was extremely proud of me and I loved him. Death terrified me and I had nightmares about worms eating my grandfather's body in the Baptist Chapel crypt. I would awake sweating and screaming with fear. My mother was frequently too drunk to hear my screams even though she shared the same bed but my grandmother would take me into her bed mentioning something about 'worming you in the morning.'

Next day cod-liver oil and malt duly followed as a routine treatment for worms and all psychological ills. Theodore growled something about 'being spoiled to death' and children needing discipline. Again, as always, I felt confused by adult interpretations of young people's behaviour.

What I knew was that both Anna and Pearl's families were so 'normal' compared to mine and I desperately wished I was them, with parents like theirs and with brothers and sisters to confide in when things got tough. Life seemed so unfair.

My grandfather, Elwyn Thomas, had had little respect for modern-day political authority and blamed the landed gentry for the poverty of the rural population. His conviction was that the gentry and the pit owners colluded to keep the average person poor and subservient to the needs of the wealthy and well-connected. He was a great believer and supporter of an educated workforce with equality of opportunity. He was an avid reader of both 'The Times' and 'The News Chronicle'.

When he became ill, he took to his bed or sometimes to his badly scratched and battered leather armchair in the corner of the kitchen next to the lead grate fireplace. There he would entertain me with stories about Tonypandy and the Chartist Riots, about Tum Shun Cattee and the fight of the Welsh Martyrs to manage their own affairs. My grandfather was passionate about political issues and the rights of the working class. He was a staunch supporter of Aneurin Bevan - he called him 'Nye' - and his commitment to a national health service for all people, regardless of wealth and status. Nye's roots were steeped in the poverty of the Welsh valleys; he had commitment to his office because he believed in justice and equality for the under-privileged.

I struggled hard to follow my grandfather's views, failing to glean any inkling of the disappointment he felt in his own lack of achievement, in part due to ill health. Sadly, my head was too full of the immediate trivia of the day to take in many of his erudite arguments. But there was something at gut level that I did understand, the flow of raw emotion and the importance of believing in something outside of the material and the mundane. However much I sought to repress it, the notion of truth and justice would be the catalyst that formulated my thinking into my teenage years and beyond.

The local baronet and largest landowner in the county was Sir Robert (known as 'Sir Rob') Fenton. He was a substantial property owner and he leased out farms and their adjacent cottages to agricultural workers in the area. In addition to his own magnificent residence, secluded by eighteen-foot walls, Sir Rob owned a lime quarry and a public house as well as having a share in a coal mine and all the trout and salmon fishing rights in the area.

My grandfather had worked for the baronet's late father, Sir Raoul Fenton. He disliked his employer's son - his former private pupil - maintaining that Sir Rob was 'an empty vessel with little learning.'

"Rob's as thick as they come Sian, but shrewd mind you, very shrewd".

He also maintained that Sir Rob was 'not to be trusted with the ladies' and that he was 'a snob on nothing other than his father's name'.

"Mark my words, Sian my love", he would frequently repeat, "young snobby Rob will get through every penny of his father's and grandfather's fortune. There'll be nothing left for the next generation. It's bad money, made on the backs of the poor. They will lose it, mark my words, but unfortunately I won't be here to see it".

I desperately hoped I would not be there to see it either but thousands of miles away with Jean Simmons and Cary Grant in Hollywood.

My grandparents had purchased a small piece of land from Sir Raoul during the time when they were in his employment. They believed that they might one day be able to build a home on the land they had scrimped and saved over many years to acquire. Predictably, my grandfather had originally rejected the idea of a land purchase from Sir Raoul, claiming it was against his principles. However, my grandmother had insisted saying that she was 'in the family way' and they needed some security for their future. They could not eat principles. If Sir Raoul died suddenly or decided to leave the country, what would happen to them? My grandmother's arguments won the day and they bought ten acres of land from Sir Raoul. 'The land' was about a five-minute walk from Davy Cottage, where my family lived and it continued to be a bone of contention between my mother, my grandmother and Theodore for as long as I can remember.

"I will leave you nothing when I die", my grandmother would say accusingly to my mother. "You will squander everything with your stupidity and passion for 'n'er do wells. How can I trust you? Any legacy from us will go to Sian; she has more sense in her little finger than you have in your whole body."

"What about me?" Theodore would interject if the squabble took place in his presence. "I come before Sian and I don't agree. Who pays the bloody bills in this house?"

He would mumble this last objection into his boots as he feared his mother's wrath.

Theodore was no match for the scathing tongue of Geraldine Thomas when aroused. Outbursts like these certainly did not help my relationship with my mother who resented my grandmother's pride in me and in my achievements. The conflict between us grew steadily worse, lasting until my grandmother's death in 1966. I so wish things had been different between us but I had to deal with life as it was, rather than how I wanted it to be.

After the death of my grandfather, I always felt sad at Baptist Chapel Services. Sometimes I cried a little into my hymn book, the pain of grief searing into my breastbone so hard that I felt a stabbing pain in my chest and an emptiness that none of the living adults around me came even close to filling.

My grandmother obviously cared for me but her constant squabbles with my mother upset and depressed me as I was torn between the two of them. My mother threatened to leave but my grandmother laughed aloud and said she wouldn't be able to take such a grand step on her own without someone to lean on and make decisions for her. My grandmother also told her that she could sleep in 'Bill the Boat's field' for all she cared but I would remain at the family home.

The atmosphere was bleak at that time, redolent with undercurrents of bitter resentment and hurt pride but I had two good friends who helped me forget home life and engage in the activities I loved most: walking, swimming in the river, playing tennis and imitating some of the local characters. It was harmless fun because they were unaware of it and it made us laugh a lot. I was able to distract myself with some silliness of the moment because I was an eleven-year-old child but I continued to mourn my grandfather's passing throughout my teenage years.

On Sunday afternoons, my grandmother insisted that I attend Sunday School and this I did - excuse the pun - religiously until I was fourteen when I discovered the mega-famous Everly Brothers. No teenager worthy of being described 'groovy' would include chapel worship among their weekly activities. In rural areas in the mid-1950s, most girls wore long knee-socks well into their teens. Many were ignorant of male anatomy and believed that pregnancy was an unfortunate result of sitting next to an 'interested' (rather a difficult concept to define) male on a bus. Hormonal changes, bodily secretions and sexual matters were an unspoken taboo in most households at the time, and the gyrating hips of Elvis and Cliff belonged to city life far away.

'Sunday tea' after Sunday school consisted of cucumber and tinned salmon sandwiches, jelly - sometimes pink blancmange - with fresh cream. There were strawberries and raspberries from the garden in June and July, gooseberries and blackcurrants in July and August and sweet red apples from my grandmother's orchard. The three of us were still not averse to entering other people's gardens for fruit, although this was usually instigated by me, rather than by Anna or Pearl. Anna was always worried about distressing her mother if we were caught whilst Pearl blithely followed what we did, unless her brother Dean was on board to tell tales of course. Once Pearl was out of earshot of her family, she could breathe freely. So many times, the raucous voice of Dora Jones had caught us as we were sneaking out the back door of the caff.

"Per...arrl, take Dean with you."

Unbeknown to me, Pearl resented both her parents and this had a lot to do with her brother Dean. Dean was eighteen months younger and for whatever reason, he quickly grew out of parental control. By the time he was nine he was cheeky to neighbours and a constant nightmare to any creature with four legs and a tail. The only person who could control him was his father but Wilf Jones rarely bothered with this inconvenience unless it affected him directly.

It was not unusual to hear his wife Dora yelling from their residence at the back of the café. "Dean's kicked me Wilf, after what you told him last time. Wilf, he's squashed the pastry on those pork pies again; Palethorpes won't take the returns now. Dean, stop it ... your father won't let you go to the fair after this! Wilf, tell him, he's opening the Liquorice Allsorts box upside down – they're all going to end up on the floor. I knew it!"

And so on and on it went. Round and round went the colourless carousel of domestic grind.

Dora Jones had been a very good-looking woman in the first flush of youth. She had been described on more than one occasion as a dead ringer for Jennifer Jones, the American film star. I remember seeing a film once with Jennifer Jones called *'Gone to Earth'* and the plot centred on the heroine's love for a pet fox and how she tried to save it from a pack of hounds. There was indeed an uncanny resemblance between Jennifer and Dora Jones but it was confined to looks alone. I could not imagine Dora saving any creature, let alone a fox. Instead, I could imagine Dora saying to her husband: "Shall I get a collar made out of this fox, Wilf? With the meat left we could make a stew for the lorry drivers; they wouldn't know it from beef, would they?"

Wilf Jones was fat and sandy-haired with the biggest head I have ever seen in my life. He had the unfortunate habit of expelling air from his pursed lips when worried or irritated.

"Putt...putt..." Wilf would ruminate, "putt... putt... putt..." as he sliced the ham with the manual slicer and tossed chips with burnt edges onto customers' plates. Dora, on the other hand, was very proud of the now fading resemblance between herself and Jennifer Jones but she carried the movie star identity a little too far. After numerous glasses of home-made wine in the evening that Dean slyly plied her with when she wasn't looking (to put her in a good mood and leave him alone), she would often launch into anecdotes about her employment many years ago as a Nippy at the Lyons Corner House on the Strand in London during the Second World War. She claimed that frequently customers would stop and ask for her autograph, assuming she was Jennifer Jones. What never occurred to me to ask as a naive eleven-year-old, was why Londoners assumed that Jennifer Jones would abandon Hollywood, don a Nippy uniform, speak with the accent of the Welsh mining valleys and proceed to serve them at table.

One could fill a book with the confabulations of Dora Jones. But one must add that these tales were rarely told when she was sober and probably served as light relief from lorry driver talk she heard all day long in the cafe.

She was in her mid-thirties when she met Wilf Jones, newly demobbed from the RAF where he had been employed as a cook. They made an ill-matched couple and spiteful gossip was rife about 'Dora going round the orchard and ending up with the crab apple'.

At this time in the 1950s, the temperamental flickering and flashing of the black and white TV set in the corner of the Jones' living-room provided little entertainment. During the mid-sixties, the television transmitters in South Wales were allocated better positions and as cathode ray images became clearer and more powerful, they were followed by a wider choice of programmes. However, stories about 'Jennifer Jones' and Dora's one encounter with the serial killer John Christie on a bus near 10 Rillington Place, continued to entertain us more than the television on Saturday nights and well into our teenage years.

Dean was a tease, and most of all he shamed and tormented his older sister. Dean was not interested in academic work or sport but on reflection, it is possible that he resented his sister's passing the Eleven Plus when he and all nine of his cousins dismally failed this important academic milestone leading to the secretly coveted ladder of social mobility. In spite of his naughtiness, Dean was still more of a favourite with his mother than Pearl was. But Pearl's Eleven Plus success had given Dora an opportunity to have what she most wanted: attention and freedom to boast about both her daughter's achievements together with the newly acquired 'hoover' from the takings of the cafe.

Dora's sister was nicknamed 'Brenda the Boast' when still at elementary school and Dora longed to overtake her sister in the boast stakes. But Brenda outdid Dora every time - serial killer or no serial killer. It was not uncommon for Dora to meet an acquaintance in the street, where she would stop and boast about anything that came into her head that day, including her daughter being so intelligent that she knew more than her teachers. She held her audience alert with histrionic head movements and extensive hand gestures.

The only fly in the ointment was Dean who would impulsively blurt out: "Dad said we haven't paid for that yet" or "She never said *that* Mam!"

Dean's interjections annoyed Dora so much that she started arguing with her son in front of her listener and curious passers-by. "Shut up Dean!" she'd yell, "just shut up - I'm talking!"

Once when Dora was boasting louder and longer than usual outside a butcher's shop, Dean became excessively bored. Without warning, he suddenly sprinted into the shop crammed with Saturday morning customers inspecting a Sunday joint. He jerked a pig's head from a metal peg just inside the door and to the far left of the shop window. With his trophy held aloft, Dean dashed out and up the street, leaving his mother oblivious to his actions as she was in the middle of a boast story. He threw the pig's head into the doorway of a snooty draper's shop. The draper was sycophantically engaged with 'a county customer', unaware of the unsightly pig's head with its ultimate expression of terror and streaks of dried blood from its neck blocking the entrance to her quality premises. But as time passed, she began to notice passers-by gathering outside her shop, sniggering and pointing. The draper approached the shop entrance, losing her composure completely when she spotted the pig's head. Her rush to dispose of the offending creature caused her to ladder one of her perfectly straight-seamed nylon stockings. She hurled such angry abuse - startling those who had believed up until then that the draper was 'so prim and proper that butter wouldn't melt in her mouth!' The butter had melted all right, but the cause of the melt had conveniently hidden himself from sight so that no reprimands could follow. But the draper was suspicious; she had caught sight of Dora Jones in the street.

In the weeks, months and years to follow, the draper speculated to all and sundry -even newcomers to Foistneth - how Dora Jones' son was responsible for events of that particular morning and he should have gone to Borstal for what he did. The draper never ate pork or as much as looked at a pig again, even china ones, without feelings of nausea and revulsion.

Dora was asked by sales assistants and neighbours time and time again to control her son but she appeared unable to carry out any consistent parental discipline. Pearl was always told to 'give in to your brother as you're older and you know what he's like.' This gave Dean carte blanche to behave badly towards his sister, with minimal parental intervention. It also meant that when Pearl had any free time to spend with us, Dean would have to be included. The diktat was: 'If Pearl comes so does Dean, otherwise Pearl has to stay.'

Pearl greatly resented her parents' attitude towards her and all three of us were very annoyed at Dean's tagging along. Dean also told tales to his parents so we had to be careful about what we said and did.

Without Dean, we had a wonderful time picnicking in woods, exploring the riverbank, collecting wild rhubarb and swinging on the rotating arm of the Foistneth cesspit. With Dean there we had to restrict our movements as he was wild and likely to do himself an injury. Once, we were all grounded for a month when Dean fell into the cesspit after attempting to fish out used condoms. Only now do I realise what risks we children took with our physical safely. We could have drowned in the cesspit or in the river; we could have impaled ourselves on the spiked iron gates protecting the village waterworks. All generations had braved the terrifying walk across the village water pipes with no handrail and spanning a deep river, sometimes in flood. Nevertheless, we were all fortunate enough to survive our reckless thwarting of danger during our childhood years.

Chapter 3

Music: *'What do you want'?* Adam Faith (1959)

There were few Jews in our rural area and the nearest synagogue was forty miles away, in Cardiff. In agricultural South Wales of the 1950s few people owned motor cars and a journey of forty miles was synonymous with travelling to New York. Anna's father was one of the two village doctors whilst her mother was a housewife. Anna's parents owned a motorcar and they went to synagogue - 'shul' they called it - as frequently as they could in order to stay in touch with the Jewish community and to participate in religious festivals. They had to stay over with friends each time on Friday nights as their religion forbade them to drive on the Sabbath. They only kept kosher on religious festivals as kosher food was difficult to get hold of without a great deal of forward planning.

I sensed that Anna's mother tolerated her daughter's friends but she did not really care for us. However, Juliet Klein wanted her children to have friends and Anna appeared to have bonded well with Pearl and myself. She was less morose and withdrawn when we were around.

Anna's older brother had learning difficulties. He was diagnosed as 'mentally handicapped' - now he would be described as autistic'- and educated at home. Anna was the middle child. Her younger brother was born when she was nine years old and attending Elementary School in the village. I envied her so much, being an only child myself.

I asked my mother why she didn't marry again so that I too could have a baby brother like Anna. My mother looked amazed, lost for words - but my grandmother was rarely caught off guard.

"First of all," she explained sternly, "your mother is not yet divorced from your father which is just as well because she would likely find an even worse 'n'er do well' - difficult as it may appear to those of sane mind. Secondly, Anna Klein's father is a doctor and with their income they can afford another child".

She then ventured, but in a more conciliatory way, that a baby brother could turn out to be 'a little monster like Dean' and that I would grow tired of him in time. This certainly clinched the argument as far as I was concerned. I detested Dean so much that I never broached the subject of baby brothers again.

Anna's parents spoke German to each other and English to their children. Anna could understand some German words and was able to roughly fathom out the gist of a discourse - a skill that became highly valued when as teenagers with an agenda, we wanted to be forewarned of any objections in order to prepare a defence. Anna's father was liked and respected by the village community although some farmers continued stubbornly to cling to the belief that Dr Klein had supported Hitler and that all Germans were Nazis. The Kleins did not mix much with village folk and after Anna had completed her 'O' levels at the age of sixteen, they moved to Cardiff where Dr Klein bought into a large medical practice and Anna's younger brother Myron was able to attend Jewish School.

During her childhood, Anna learned more about the religious rituals and doctrines of Welsh Baptists and the Church of England than her own faith. One year she begged to attend the Harvest Thanksgiving festival at the Baptist Chapel with Pearl and myself. Anna's mother was uneasy with her request but Dr Klein approved the idea. I later learned that he wisely believed it to be a good public relations exercise to thwart anti-German attitudes among some parishioners.

I attended because my grandfather had been a staunch chapel supporter. Pearl's parents were also chapel, although her mother only went because she was sweet on one of the chapel deacons. Her father only ever attended the chapel for funerals where he could offer his services as both bearer and caterer.

The three of us (unbeknown to Anna's family) would sit on the upstairs balcony of the chapel next to my mother whose attention was not on the religious service but on the clandestine interaction in the downstairs pews between Pearl's mother and the deacon, Tim Lewis. Dean delighted in tearing up a hymn book and rolling the pages into 'spills' to light my grandmother's coal fire later when we returned to my home for Sunday tea. But sometimes he would toss the spills one by one from the chapel balcony, precision aiming at the plumaged hats of the ample-bosomed ladies sitting downstairs within target range of the overhanging balcony. A startled few would look upwards, staring outraged at the three of us giggling overhead - Dean was smaller than us and could scarcely be seen from the downstairs pews. As usual he was exonerated from all blame whilst we were sharply scolded with threats of privileges withdrawn.

After the service, there was usually a discussion on the quality of the minister's sermon which took place outside the main entry doors of the chapel or sometimes inside the adjoining vestry where tea was served. We three became quickly bored with hanging around the vestry for home-made Welsh cakes and sugary cups of tea. We would slip out the minute Dean went to the lavatory (we were getting good at giving him the slip) and we sped along the partially submerged path nestling under overgrown grass to the part of the graveyard that housed an imposing marble tombstone in a very large rectangular enclosure. The rusting iron-fenced structure encircling the tombstone held tens of thousands of bleached white pebbles that we loved to grab and pelt each other with when the adults weren't looking. A tall and menacing granite angel stood proudly on the top of its marble pedestal, a cracked toe creeping stealthily from the stone folds of its flowing robe. Faded gilt lettering below proclaimed the date of death and carried a short verse from the bible together with the social status of the deceased: *Captain Nathaniel Ferris-Brown of Oak House, timber merchant, generous employer, loving father and husband. Beloved of this parish.*

The angel's overly large wings stuck out stiffly as if the sculptor had had difficulty gauging their balancing position. Its stony expression was grim and calculating. I never liked angels after seeing this one. Perhaps it was a fitting symbol as I know for a fact that my family disliked the Ferris-Browns for their behaviour towards the poor and vulnerable through whom they had made their fortune by selling poor quality timber, almost as much as they disliked Sir Rob.

On that day our intentions were benign; all we wanted was to have 'a good giggle' and discuss matters of high importance to eleven-year-olds whilst escaping boredom and adult idiosyncrasies. But as we excitedly rushed towards our menacing angel, I stopped suddenly and gasped. I clearly witnessed Pearl's mother pulling out of the arms of 'the delightful deacon' who was partially hidden behind the rigid span of one of the angel's wings.

Anna also took in the scene and we discussed this episode many times over a bottle of wine in our mature years but at the time, Pearl seemed unaware of what was happening. "Our Mam," she said calmly, "what are you doing here with the deacon? Dean was looking for you to take him to the toilet."

"Why didn't you take him?" screeched Dora Jones, her face crimson with obvious embarrassment. "You children are all the same, you want to do nothing; at your age I was 'elping' my parents, I was working...."

The theme was very familiar and well-rehearsed. We contritely returned to the chapel whilst the deacon feigned interest in something and wandered off in the opposite direction. But I knew Dora was embarrassed by our presence and for once I felt very powerful. I had a feeling that over the next few weeks we would be able to off-load Dean without too much opposition from his mother.

This indeed turned out to be the case whilst my own mother, delighted by the story, quizzed me again and again on the finer details: 'how far behind the angel's wings and close to the tomb were they?' 'Did she still have her hat on?' 'Did it look as if he was pulling up his trousers when you surprised them?' I enjoyed her attention but when I yelled at her - believing that the Sanatogen had impaired her short-term memory yet again – repeating that it was Dean who had gone to the toilet, not the deacon - my mother became annoyed, telling me 'to stop being so bloody silly or you'll never pass for the Grammar School'.

Such are the anomalies of life and a child's struggle to comprehend the incomprehensible behaviour of those they love and depend on.

Anna's mother worked in her husband's surgery in the mornings. One of the local villagers cleaned their house twice a week and a privately hired teacher worked with their autistic son, Lawrence. Dr Harry Klein was short and stocky with a magnificent mane of thick blonde hair. Mrs Klein was pale, dark and willowy, not unlike Anna but better looking and without the 'offending nose' that caused the teasing on the school bus.

Just like my own mother, and totally unlike Pearl's, Mrs Klein did not make the best of herself and wore dowdy clothes that did not suit her. She was an educated woman and it was rumoured that she had met her husband at medical school in Berlin and that she had married Harry Klein when they were both doctors in-training but had dropped out of medical school and did not qualify. Local people often speculated as to why. It was known that the Kleins left Germany hurriedly in 1938, a year before the outbreak of the Second World War. Anti-Semitism was rife in Berlin, resulting in the subsequent internment and segregation of German Jews. Harry was greatly alarmed by what was happening with Jews barred from holding any kind of professional office or owning businesses and Harry's parents, brother and family, his two married sisters and their families, all left hurriedly for Palestine in 1937 leaving most of what they owned behind in Germany.

Harry would have gone with them if his wife had agreed but Juliet stubbornly believed things would change and that the German people would eventually tire of Hitler and the Nazis. Also, Juliet's parents and younger sister stayed on in Berlin, stubbornly oblivious to the ever-increasing danger to their own survival. In the end Harry and Juliet were forced to flee at the end of 1938 with special permits obtained by a non-Jewish friend with influence at Nazi headquarters. They had lost their opportunity to go to Palestine but England agreed to take them because Harry was a physician. Juliet's parents, her sister, her nephew and nieces all perished in death camps in Poland. No individual with even a tenuous genetic link to Juliet survived the Holocaust and she, herself, continued to live most of her life under the imagined threat of persecution. She was anxious - unable to relax -and even after the War, feared an extreme right-wing political movement in Britain with power to persecute Jews. Juliet feared many things: illness of her children, her husband's loss of income and social rejection of her autistic son. But the one thing she never feared was her own death.

Juliet always kept her eyes on the ground when out of the surgery and her own home. She responded awkwardly to any apparent gestures of friendliness on the part of the villagers. She feared everyone and trusted no-one. Although ostensibly courteous, Juliet presented as a nervous and joyless woman with no sense of humour. She was very aware that her attitude to non-Jewish strangers was unlikely to change because she lived in constant fear of a British Holocaust. When Bill Hayley was singing 'Rock Around The Clock' and causing riots at the Pavilion Cinema in Foistneth, Juliet was sitting terrified at home, believing that the advent of Rock and Roll might cause a state backlash against the predominance of Jews running the film and music industries in Hollywood. She feared this would lead to the cessation of individual liberty because Jews would be blamed for 'Rock and Roll' which in turn would result in racist targeting and deportation of all immigrants from Great Britain.

Only those who have suffered the daily agony of persecution and lost their entire families, could possibly understand the overwhelming daily dread experienced by someone in Juliet Klein's position.

Prior to South Wales, the Kleins had lived in East London for six years after their arrival in Britain but left the city because of the bombing. Juliet was particularly concerned by their son's distressed reaction to the whines and whistles of the bombs falling within yards of their home.

"Our child will die!" Juliet would scream at her husband as they headed for the nearest air-raid shelter. "Hitler will win if he kills our children here!"

Harry would attempt to calm her fears by rational argument or at other times by expressing empathy with her distress and by caressing again and again her long luxuriant dark hair.

"Hitler will never win because Churchill is half American. Britain will fight to the end. Juliet, we will never, ever give up. We will be certain here of a secure future for Lawrence and any other children we may have, believe me."

Juliet took some comfort from his words but her piercing ache was like an open wound. Part of her remained unconvinced, wrapped up as she was in past pain of loss and the terror of an unpredictable future.

Eventually, Harry Klein found an affordable GP practice with an attached comfortable family residence in what seemed to him a safe rural area of South Wales. The Kleins moved to our village in 1944, and their daughter Anna was born in 1946. But Juliet could never rid herself of her intrinsic anxiety, insecurity and fear. Only Anna knew what havoc her mother's demons inflicted upon the family dynamics but it was Anna herself, who experienced more of her mother's passionate and irrational outbursts than any other member of her family. Because of his emotional deficits, Lawrence was less finely tuned to his mother's distress than his sister was.

The family move to Cardiff occurred when the Kleins' youngest child was six. Subsequently, Juliet became less emotionally vulnerable, mainly because of the support given by the city's Jewish Community. Juliet Klein was a skilled violinist and in Cardiff she joined a small orchestra which gave her the longed-for opportunity to express her sadness through music. It gave her release and a sense of worth and purpose that was lacking in her former village life where Juliet had no role other than as 'the doctor's wife, neither Church nor Chapel', which was how the village community was religiously divided. It annoyed Juliet that some villagers were given openly to pitying Lawrence, adopting patronising attitudes that made her shake with unspeakable rage. Juliet's dedication to the protection of Lawrence left little emotional space for Anna who felt she did not want to distress her mother by complaining about her tormentors on the school bus.

When the three of us became friendly and were officially recognised as 'a gang' by our peers, the verbal attacks on Anna became less frequent. But few witnessed Anna's sadness at her mother's smothering of her own spontaneity or witnessed my own frustration at being my mother's emotional punch-bag. Both of us envied Pearl, a handmaiden to 'Jennifer Jones', who demanded that Pearl work in the family cafe on Saturdays and tend to her brother's needs, especially when Dora had secret encounters with the chapel deacon for outside these demands, Dora was cheerful enough and quite prepared to leave her daughter alone to get on with her own life while Wilf loved what he called 'a spot on the gee-gees' on Saturday afternoons, leaving Pearl to mind the caff for a couple of hours before closing. Compared to Anna and myself, Pearl's life appeared like a bed of roses. But then, none of us ever walked in each other's moccasins as the Native American metaphor goes. If we had, we might have reached very different conclusions.

My father kept some sort of erratic contact with my mother for about fifteen months after his disappearance from the family home. We learned later that he had joined the Merchant Navy. My grandmother mentioned something about 'an ugly doll' he sent as a present for my ninth birthday. My grandmother returned the doll to him asking him not to contact us again as his wife was taking legal action against him. My grandparents insisted that my mother sign the legal document petitioning for a legal separation on grounds of desertion. My father attempted a half-hearted reconciliation by appealing to my mother but my grandmother had anticipated this and refused all communication on my mother's behalf in a letter executed in her exquisite copper-plate handwriting. My grandparents had persuaded my mother to sign the letter terminating all contact with him after one of her drinking binges. At that point she was incapable of knowing what she was signing. She may well have signed the separation document herself on a whim but my grandmother did not want to risk placing herself in a subordinate position, in the power of my mother. For once, my grandmother allowed my mother to drink with impunity and actually bought the wine herself - at least that is how my mother remembers it. What I can recall from those times is that my father faded out of our lives and gradually out of my memory.

Any questions relating to my father's whereabouts or intentions would stimulate harsh retorts and dismissiveness from the adults still in my life who found it difficult, apart from my grandfather, to demonstrate love and caring even though they felt it in different ways - even Uncle Theo who had no idea how to relate to a child.

Any question put to Theo about my father instantly triggered his standard reply: "Cliff Bayley was a bad lot. He stole your grandmother's silver to sell for gambling." He rarely added more about Cliff other than the list of things assumed missing from my mother's and my grandparents' houses. I got the impression that if the milk was missing from the doorstep, Theo would invent a theory of its disappearance based on my father's gambling habit.

The three of us would collapse into laughter and imitate Theo's mumbling flat tone when we misplaced anything. We would say: "Who's had the marbles? I know they were here a moment ago".

"Ah, Cliff Bayley's had them and sold them for gambling. He's a bad lot!"

Mrs Klein would sharply admonish Anna if she overhead our banter. Dora thought it plain silly and suggested Pearl grow up and apply herself to washing dishes and 'elping in the caff' but my mother took great pleasure in my imitation of Theo.

In time, I ceased asking questions about my father. I invented an imaginary father who was loving and kind but distant. Sometimes I told my school friends that I believed him dead as happened in the novels of so many of my favourite 19th century heroines. Apart from Jane Austin novels, where fathers had character weaknesses and tended to cling onto senility and torment their daughters, most literary dads were well and truly departed when the heroine was a child. Such were the losses and eventual strengths experienced by Becky Sharp, Catherine Earnshaw and Jane Eyre. No one thought the worst of them for it. I used to desperately wish that I had been born in the 19th rather than the 20th century. Oh, the innocent stupidity of childhood!

Dr Klein was not our GP as old Dr Townsend had always looked after our family. There were only two doctors in the village practice at this time. Dr Townsend was about twenty years older than Dr Klein and he suffered from rheumatism in the knees. Consequently, almost all domiciliary visits were carried out by Dr Klein, who was reputed to be wonderful with children and the elderly. But my grandmother disliked him. He was called out to my grandfather on one occasion though and on two further occasions he was called out to my mother - both in the same year. He came to my mother after one of her heavy drinking binges that made her hallucinate, convinced she could 'fly out of the window, across the garden to perfect peace.'

I vividly remember my grandmother shaking me awake in the dead of night. "Sian, go and fetch the doctor, your mother has been taken seriously ill! Theodore isn't here. He's staying somewhere tonight".

My grandmother had aroused me from a deep sleep so it took me a while to register what she was actually asking me to do.

"Gran, it's dark - how can I go on my own? I can't see!"

There was no electric light in the village at this time because Sir Rob had refused to allow the transformer carrying electricity to the village to be constructed on his land. Sir Rob's explanation was that he did not want to blight the panoramic beauty of the local landscape with its picturesque hills and meandering river by allowing a monster pylon carrying electricity to be sited there but my grandfather insisted it was more about squeezing a higher price out of the local council than protection of the environment.

On my grandfather's insistence, it was finally decided that my grandmother would accompany me as it was obvious that I was terrified of walking the two miles to the doctor's house along a very gloomy road with few houses and next to a wood I believed was full of ghosts. My grandfather always said there was more to fear from the living than the dead, but I didn't believe him. He insisted that he was well enough to supervise my mother's 'shenanigans' and was adamant that his wife accompany me to fetch the doctor as her plea for a home visit at such an hour would be more plausible than the explanations of a child.

My mother growled as we discussed the plan of action. "You bloody bitch, I'll see you in hell!"

She retched up blood into the tin bowl held by my grandmother. I am so very glad that my grandfather had taken the lead for once and had made a decision and that my grandmother had agreed to it.

We managed to raise Dr Klein by hammering hard on the front door. Anna's mother eventually opened it in her dressing-gown and was shocked to see me standing there frightened and pale-faced, accompanied by my grandmother. I can't remember much about what followed but we returned to Davy Cottage in Dr Klein's car. He didn't speak to us along the way other than to ask about my mother's sudden illness. He was usually friendly towards me as he knew Anna and I were best friends but he was silent on this occasion. It was evident that he disliked my grandmother and the imperious tone she adopted when feeling threatened or embarrassed.

Dr Klein examined my mother and whatever happened next I was totally ignorant of because I was sent to bed. It was a Sunday evening and I had 'school in the morning'.

A week or two later when I was playing outside at Anna's, Dr Klein called me into the house and asked me to sit opposite him on a chair in the kitchen. He had a newspaper spread out on the long wooden kitchen table and I could hear the voice of Mrs Klein in the living-room as she read aloud to Lawrence. "He was H O T", I heard her say, "hot". There was no response. "The sun is hot," she enunciated. "People are on the beach; they want to swim".

"Knickers on", retorted Lawrence, "all kickers on".

"A swimsuit", stated Juliet pedantically in an expressionless voice. "They are wearing swimsuits".

I started to giggle but Dr Klein's expression held no humour. "Sian", he said gently, slowly leaning towards me across the shiny surface of the polished table, "your mother is an alcoholic and unless she stops drinking, she will die. Your grandmother refuses to accept this very simple fact. Your mother is also clinically depressed. She can be treated with medication for her depressive state but she must stop drinking if it is to work. What influence do you have with her?"

His piercing grey eyes stared out under bushy blonde eyebrows. His direct eye contact confused me. I said I didn't know what he meant and timidly asked for clarification.

"Don't buy alcohol for your mother however hard she pleads and don't believe her lies and excuses. Give her your love and support but do not give her drink or collude with her distorted view of the world. Tell your grandparents about her pressures on you to buy alcohol. They need to realise that unless she stops drinking she will die of liver disease. Her liver is inflamed from abuse of alcohol but she is also a depressed woman who needs medication."

He paused for a few seconds looking at me, suddenly struck by my youth and immaturity.

"I will tell your grandparents", he said kindly.

I felt tears well up behind my eyes, not because of my mother's diagnosis (I hadn't really understood the seriousness of it or the technical terms) but because of the empathic gentleness and understanding shown to me. For once, I was not ridiculed or emotionally battered by adult demands. My confusion, my pain and fear were understood by somebody else.

After two subsequent hospital admissions and many years later, my mother eventually became abstinent from alcohol. I was seventeen at the time. However, she replaced alcohol with a then liberally prescribed antidepressant called Diazepam, or Valium as it is more commonly known. My mother built up an addiction to Valium which lasted for the rest of her life. So who was my mother? To be honest, I never really knew her. She was always mood altered by some substance: alcohol and cigarettes, then Valium and cigarettes. The addictive substance changed that is all. My mother was forever a stranger to me. I never ever knew my mother.

During my childhood I lived in dread of two things happening. The first was my grandmother's death and the second was the horror of the tall brick kitchen chimney keeling over onto the roof of the cottage and killing us all while we slept.

My grandmother said that by the law of averages, the chimney was equally likely to fall backwards into the garden as forwards onto the roof. My grandfather disagreed, saying that its positioning meant that mathematically it could only fall forwards.

I believed my grandfather and quaked with fear at night during thunderstorms, believing that the fateful chimney would crash onto the roof at any minute extinguishing our very existence. Fortunately, mathematics defeated the chimney in the same way as it always defeated me at school.

Chapter 4

Music: 'Only the Lonely'. Roy Orbison (1961)

When we were eleven, it was rumoured among our friends that girls had periods and bled every month. Anna, however, had this information from her mother so we knew it was probably trustworthy. I broached the subject with my mother, hoping for some confirmation but she flew into a rage, accusing Mrs Klein of being 'a dirty woman and a liar!' My perplexity was complete when my grandmother, on this one occasion, refused to discuss the matter and referred me to my mother for advice and explanation. Neither came. But I knew the score and awaited my first period anxiously. It happened when I was twelve. Mrs Klein provided me with a sanitary belt and sanitary towels because I was too ashamed to ask my mother for them. Pearl didn't have this problem as Dora had discussed 'women's things' some years before with her daughter. But Dean proved to be the usual menace by hunting through personal items in his sister's room. Once he fished out a box of sanitary towels and rushed into the caff' yelling: "Dad, what are these? I've found them in our Pearl's drawer!"

We three fell in love with film stars and rock stars of the day as well as boys in short trousers on the school bus. But I always remembered my annoyance with Anna who expressed surprise at my infatuation with a local Grammar School boy called Wyn Jones.

"I thought you liked Dr Kildare (Richard Chamberlain)", she taunted, "Wyn doesn't look like Dr Kildare at all."

"Dr Kildare is in Hollywood, Wyn is here."

I dreamt about Wyn as much as I dreamt about Dr Kildare but both were equally remote and oblivious to my passion. Wyn dealt me my first rejection in love by showing a preference for Wendy Probert, a blonde, petite Secondary Modern girl with a snub nose. Believe it or not, they married nine years later and ran a garage together in Foistneth. They had four children and spent all their lives within a twenty-mile radius of where they were born. I always swore that such a fate would never be mine. But I cried a lot about Wyn as I really believed he fancied me and did not know what I had done wrong.

"Wyn is a typical country bumpkin", Anna used to say. "He wouldn't know how to appreciate anyone like you. Forget him, he's not worth crying over!" I would agree with her openly but still desire Wyn's affection and go home and cry myself to sleep. What could I do to make Wyn notice me? Pearl suggested I invite him to the annual school dance and ask him to bring along his friends so that it was not an obvious invitation but 'a teenager scene'. It worked. Wyn came and brought two male friends. One of them fancied Pearl and the two danced together all night. I was furious! Wyn danced only once with me and three times with another girl he met for the first time that evening. Wyn's other friend was pimply but quite pleasant and he danced with me a number of times. The boys who asked Anna to dance were usually 'brainy and boring' and most were physically unattractive. I believed myself to be prettier than Anna and was devastated when we both appeared to miss the best apples in the orchard. I didn't believe Pearl was any prettier than me and she was considerably shyer but... she attracted better looking boys. None of us were able to work out these quirks of the opposite sex.

Only soft drinks were served at the school dance but at parties in private houses, alcohol was around and on one occasion I got hopelessly drunk and spent the evening vomiting into a friend's toilet screaming that I now had 'a career of a drunk, just like the bitch - my mother!' But in spite of this degrading episode, I realised even then that I was not prepared to follow in the footsteps of my mother, wallowing in self-pity and inflicting unhappiness on myself and others. No, to survive in the real world I would need to imitate my grandmother and be in control of situations. I would need to pull the strings of the human marionettes, not allow them to pull mine. I really don't know how or when I reached this reductionist view of human relationships but whatever the initial trigger to my thinking, I learned over time to establish control before I descended into the abyss of anguish and despair so often created by other people's chaos - people I loved and people I desperately wanted to love me.

The Christmas before our sixteenth birthdays and the year of our 'O'

Level examinations was a significant milestone that we three would never forget. The Kleins did not celebrate Christmas but celebrated Chanukah, the Jewish Festival of Light. Some years Christian and Jewish festival dates coincided within a couple days of each other so we were able to exchange gifts and festive greetings without parental restrictions. Although not strictly Orthodox Jews, the Kleins had suffered enough persecution from anti-Semitic Christians to feel uncomfortable with the celebration of a Christian festival. One has to remember that we are talking about the first generation of Jewish refugees whose families had died in the Holocaust barely fifteen years earlier. Many first-generation Holocaust survivors did not really believe their children were safe outside of Israel. Anna's mother held this view but she was uncertain whether it was the time to leave Great Britain because her husband had a stable career in medicine and her children's lives appeared settled. But Juliet Klein experienced almost daily foreboding. She contemplated the future, pondering on where they might eventually end up. One thing was certain, she did not wish to remain where she was, in the little Welsh village eight miles west of Foistneth. There was no Jewish Community to provide her children with a religious education or any type of cultural bonding linked to language and heritage. Because the young Kleins were allowed no Christmas tree and were refused permission to decorate their home, Anna loved to come to my house as Uncle Theodore always purchased a Christmas tree from the local forestry - although we preferred to steal one from the Rector's garden. None of us liked the unmarried Church Rector who was pompous and overweight - stuffed full as he was with his sister's butter scones and lemon curd tarts. But if we were caught, punishment would be very harsh so we gave up on that 'Famous Five' adventure. Theodore always insisted that my mother decorate the tree, not only because she was very artistic and capable of doing what the rest of us could not, but also to keep her off the alcohol for a couple of hours. My grandmother had to ensure she was sober before she went up the ladder to place decorations on the top branches of the fir tree. Once I remember wishing she would fall and break her neck so that after the drama of her death there would be less family chaos and less pervasive melancholy. I then felt very guilty for my thoughts. But a drunk has nine lives and she survived the tree dressing each year. I used to dream that my mother was happily remarried and also Uncle Theo had a wife and two rosy-cheeked children, all smiling together in front of a large, heavily bauble-decked Christmas tree as seen at the end of the movie 'A Beautiful Life', starring James Stewart. The words of a then popular Christmas song came to mind.

'C is for the candy decked around the Christmas Tree; H is for the happiness with all the famil..ee.'

Good times; bad times. Confusing times.

It was Saturday early afternoon, 23rd December when we three congregated at my grandmother's house. The tree was dressed, the adults arguing elsewhere. We were restless and bored, after playing Snakes and Ladders for the fourth time. We longed to go out and enjoy an adventure - particularly since we were Dean free. The week before we had seen a film called 'North by Northwest' with Cary Grant, James Mason and Eva Marie-Saint. Anna had said the house used in the film reminded her of Porth Court, Sir Rob Fenton's imposing county residence. She also ventured that she had overheard a conversation between their cleaner and the butcher's delivery man saying that there were "some funny goings on at Porth Court". We later changed this into 'fanny goings on'. The stately Georgian residence was set back from the road in forty acres of rich forestry, with a river full of gleaming trout and broad-backed salmon visible below its smooth, dark surface. Sir Rob rented out the fishing rights to holiday makers and those keen on trout and salmon fishing - 'them nobs' - Dora Jones called them. The edge of the woodland and riverbank could be seen from the house but only the front bedroom windows had an uninterrupted view of the river. We decided to pay Sir Rob a visit in the hope of finding out more about 'the fanny goings on' and whether Sir Rob was breaking the law. Because of hearsay and village gossip, we all intensely disliked Sir Rob. We reached the riverbank, attempting to cross over to Sir Rob's side with a makeshift raft made from stray pieces of chipped wood. Unfortunately, the river was in flood and the raft capsized half-way across leaving us soaking wet, shivering in the brown swirling water and terrified for our own survival and worse - with the fear of parental consequences. It was now dark and bitterly cold. I silently cursed Enid Blyton who had not told us how physically uncomfortable children's adventures really were. I also cursed Hollywood that had inexplicably agreed to Eva-Marie Saint wearing stiletto heels whilst being dragged up sheer rock cliffs by Cary Grant. For God's sake, it must have been impossible agony and why on earth did I think of that when dying from hypothermia! It had been my idea to carry on across the River Usk, ignoring Anna's suggestion to turn back when the relentless force of the muddy flood decreased by the second our survival into adulthood. I alone was optimistic about us making it to the other side. I said if we kept rigidly to our charted passage across, we could do it. We would go to one of the local farmhouses and borrow a towel and then return by road. But as always, I minimised the risks and exaggerated the gains. I fell off the raft and was nearly swept away. I was barely aware of Anna screaming in dismay:

"Sian, hang on, hang on, we'll get help, hang on!"

The force of the current bashed my arm against a log and I almost lost consciousness with the pain. Then my feet got trapped under a large rock with my body upright. My positioning kept me temporarily afloat, hanging on for dear life to the rock edge. I could hear Pearl's voice in the far distance.

"Anna, one of us must get help for Sian. You stay here and I'll go. There is no point in all three of us drowning!"

Her focussed determination impressed me - even in the distressed state I was in. Pearl's role was usually to follow, not make crucial decisions. Anna appeared unusually overwhelmed and agreed to stay with me whilst Pearl would try to wade through the other half of the river to Sir Rob's estate and raise the alarm. Anna had managed to reach a moss encrusted rock with a partially flat surface. She hauled herself onto it and extended her discarded raincoat to me. But I was a little too far downstream and out of Anna's reach. I yelled in terror:

"Anna, for God's sake help me! Pray for me, God of the Jews I don't care, help me, help me!".

That afternoon I believed I was dying and so did Anna. Like myself she was becoming delirious by fear, exacerbated by the freezing cold and numbing discomfort of the river water. The dark, surging, merciless Usk continued its determined course towards the Bristol Channel sweeping along all floating debris in its path. Pearl miraculously managed to get to the other side and stumbled across Ted, Sir Rob's estate manager who lived in a small cottage overlooking the riverbank. He gasped in amazement at Anna and me flaying about in the flooded river. Pearl told us later - shrieking with laughter - that Ted had shown some reservations at our choice of hobby.

"What do you lot want to go swimming for in the Usk in December?" By this time the winter light was quickly fading and Ted realised he was unable to rescue us alone. He went to fetch Sir Rob and some of his staff. All I remember was a red bleary face of a man (I was told later it was Ted) and a soft voice of woman calling out:

"You'll be okay Sian, hang on!"

I eventually recognised the voice as that of Mattie Boyce, a very attractive divorced woman who worked part-time at 'The Spinning Knight', one of the two village public houses. Mattie was nicknamed 'Mattie the Mattress' because of her partiality for extra-marital affairs. She was recently divorced and her lack of sexual hypocrisy and scant regard for social norms and conformity, made her a constant target for village gossip. But Mattie carried on in her own way, deliberately unresponsive to the critical comments about her lifestyle. It was rumoured that Mattie was so highly sexed that some men had suffered heart attacks after spending one night with her. It was inevitable that sooner or later she would catch the eye of the notorious womaniser, Sir Rob Fenton. Theirs was a clandestine affair among un-equals. Their encounters took place at the baronet's estate when his wife was spending time at their flat in London. When Lady Fenton was in residence, they visited a discreet hotel in the vicinity of Foistneth. Fortunately, Mattie was present on this particular evening when Anna and I were pulled from the river and she was instrumental in preventing our falling ill with pneumonia. The skin on my hands was torn and bleeding from digging in and clutching the rock to steady myself; my lower body was completely numb. I had difficulty walking straight and my hands shook from tension. We were hurriedly shepherded to Sir Rob's servants' quarters and given a hot bath. We three sat in warm dressing-gowns drinking piping hot cocoa with a dash of whiskey whilst our clothes were dried on the enormous kitchen agar. I had never seen a kitchen so big in my whole life - even bigger than the Klein's. I believe my red dressing gown with the quilted sleeves that fell below my knees once belonged to her ladyship. The whiskey made me light-headed and (so my friends said) quite confident and talkative. Mattie appeared not to care that we had recognised her and it was she who had taken charge and issued orders to Sir Rob's housekeeper to provide us with hot drinks and warm clothing. She was intent on looking after us and getting us back safely to our parents. Scandalous talk was the least of her worries but it certainly was not the least of Sir Rob's. In my semi-comatose state, I could hear their arguments.

"For God's sake!" shouted Sir Rob, "do you realise that these kids could cause us a lot of trouble? One says she is the doctor's daughter! How the hell are we going to cope with this?"

"Oh, shut up!" yelled Mattie forcefully. "Do you intend killing them or what? These kids nearly drowned in your sodding river! Don't you think their parents will see you as some kind of hero for saving them? What is the matter with you? In fact, you can expect some sort of medical priority from now on from the doctor but you may have to explain the situation to Lady Fenton first."

Sir Rob retorted angrily that he already had 'medical priority' whatever that was but the mention of Lady Fenton caused him some concern. Then I passed out, blissfully unaware of any further adult machinations.

There were twelve visitors at Sir Rob's house that evening and some of them were local, but Mattie was the only person we knew both by sight and by name. Sir Rob questioned us, but he was never really sure whether we had actually recognised any of the individuals at his stately residence that fateful afternoon. We were subsequently delivered to our respective homes by Sir Rob's chauffeur and then the real trouble started. We were all interrogated but in very different ways. Mrs Klein feared the consequences to Anna's physical health saying she might die of pneumonia after her experience in the river. Dr Klein and my grandmother focussed their admonishments on personal danger and how we had demonstrated an astoundingly nonchalant attitude to danger by our defiance and stupidity in choosing to cross the river in flood. Dr Klein kept telling his daughter:

"I cannot believe you haf no common sense! You appear so much more intelligent and mature when you are at home than when you are with these two girls."

Anna told us this some weeks later, imitating her father's German accent to give more of a dramatic effect. Juliet blamed the incident on Pearl and myself, mainly accusing me because of my mother's deficiencies as a parent (this I did not learn until many years later). My mother and Dora also made accusations of stupidity, with abundant predictions of drowning in whirlpools but both were far more interested in Sir Rob's house, the chauffeur-driven car and the presence of Mattie Boyce. I said Mattie was clad only in a red lace brassiere and panties. I later added a frilly black negligee which she threw over herself when the housekeeper arrived with the cocoa. I knew this story would inflame curiosity and divert my mother from remarks concerning my immature shortcomings. My grandmother became irritated.

"Don't tell lies Sian or you'll end up like your father."

I was hurt by her cutting remark but I knew my grandmother was seriously worried about me and only she seemed aware of how close to death I had been. She showed no interest at all in Mattie Boyce.

All three of us were grounded after the incident in the river. We were forbidden to see each other for three months but we actually managed to get together again after five weeks following a great deal of begging, sulking and impracticable promises. The five weeks apart felt like years. All three of us painfully existed without the other and experienced huge pangs of loss, loneliness and boredom. The old adage 'two is company, three is a crowd' did not apply to us. There were times when we quarrelled and took sides against the odd one out but it tended to be a short-lived trivial issue and was rare. We felt incomplete when one of our number was missing. I have struggled over the years to understand both the strength and the complexity of our trio relationship but the only conclusion I reach is that we felt unconditional love for one another and had found in one another's company a basic compatibility of the kind that is rarely found, even in a partner. All three of us experienced a lack of emotional closeness to our parents, although our families, their style of parenting and our social circumstances were very different. Anna was 'put on probation' by her father and if she broke the rules again she would not be allowed to participate in any of our social activities. Dr Klein was now persuaded by his wife that they needed to move and help their children develop roots in their own culture and traditions before they became too indifferent or too rebellious. Our escapade contributed greatly to the Kleins' decision to leave the village the following summer, after Anna had completed her 'O' Levels. Following my own verbal chastisements, I swore to mend the error of my ways but my grandmother said she had little faith in my promises. Pearl was not surprised at Dora's suggested cure for her immaturity: helping out more in the shop on Saturdays. As for the Fentons, the housekeeper was pleasantly surprised (as was Lady Fenton) by the Fortnum and Mason Christmas hamper sent to Sir Rob's staff by Dr Klein that year with an accompanying note of gratitude for 'saving the children from the river.' Mattie Boyce received a thank you card from the three of us with a small box of chocolates bought from our own pocket money.

I passed my six 'O' Levels and received my one and only A grade for French. I had adored the French mistress who was an excellent teacher, open and spontaneous to the pupils eager to learn. I was more pleased for her than for myself. 'Mamselle Michelle' was neither patronising nor bullying and on one occasion when I was really upset by an incident at home, she spent time with me talking about teenage hormonal changes and clashes with parental authority. She suggested I read women's magazines that discussed these issues, although Anna was an additional fount of knowledge on that score. I was disappointed when I learned I had failed my maths 'O' level and that the only science subject I had passed was biology. I had passed 5 O Levels; Anna had passed eight, including maths, chemistry and biology. Anna only had one 'C' (history) and all the others were evenly distributed between A and B grades. Pearl passed five subjects including maths but her overall grades were lower than mine. But the aftermath of the 'O' Level examinations was an anti-climax. What would we do now? Return to school? Go to work? Take a vocational subject like shorthand typing? Anna of course would proceed through A levels to university. Pearl and I were unsure of our future and we were both tired of school. All three of us had been competitive in our academic work, trying to outdo one another. Both my own and Pearl's greatest aspiration was to score higher marks than Anna who was always in the top five of her form. Needless to say, this rarely happened as Pearl and I tended to score around the middle to lower end of the range, and very much dependent on the academic subject.

My mother's drinking got worse in the spring before my 'O' Level examinations. There was no further attempt on her part to control her alcoholism or lie about it. She only stopped drinking if the pub was closed and she had run out of money. Publicans were emphatically told by Theodore and my grandmother not to serve her or give her booze on credit. Mostly they did not. During this period my mother suffered delirium tremens from alcohol withdrawal. But there were also other equally disturbing features of alcohol abuse and that was the deceit and the lies. I will never forget the time when my mother stole my birthday money. I had hidden it in the top drawer of the chest in my bedroom because I was saving up for a shift dress that was the height of fashion at the time. My mother swore blind she would never steal from her own daughter and said she was horrified by my accusations. She said we were all against her and only her father had really understood her. I broke down and sobbed, feeling guilty. My grandmother replaced the money with Theo's help but from that time on I felt devastated and even more vulnerable in my relationship with my mother. I knew then that I could never trust her.

One night, some weeks after my sixteenth birthday, I awoke to find my mother standing in her nightdress by the dressing-table to the left of the tiny paned bedroom window. We still shared a bedroom but now we had single beds. The room usually stank of urine, sweet wine and cigarettes but inadequately camouflaged by the fragrance of lavender which my mother would spray around the room in order to get rid of the stale alcohol smell. To this day the aroma of lavender makes me retch. My mother had lit a candle so as not to wake me with the electric light beam. Sir Rob had got his asking price after all and had given permission for the electricity transformer to be sited on his land. My eyes alighted on a figure rummaging through my jewellery box. The figure held up some trinket to the candlelight - scrutinising it closely. With her dishevelled black hair touching her shoulders and the eerie white of her nightdress in the flickering candlelit darkness, the phantom was reminiscent of 'the mad woman', Mrs Rochester, in the novel Jane

Eyre. I let out a rasping shriek of horror, louder even than Charlotte Bronte's heroine. I woke up the household and within minutes Theodore and my grandmother came running into our bedroom. My grandmother's greying black hair was braided into one thick plait hanging down her back and she had not stopped even to put on her dressing-gown to cover her nightdress which she usually did out of modesty. She was frantic as she shouted: "For God sakes Sian, what is going on here? Alice, what are you doing?" Her voice suddenly dropped an octave.

"Alice, why is Sian like this?"

"She's stealing Sian's things again to sell for booze", growled Theodore in his inimitably tactless way. "She'd steal the bread out of the mouth of her own kid. You are despicable, Alice, do you know that? Despicable. That stupid old man spoiled you rotten!"

Theodore never missed a trick when it came to blaming my grandfather. They had never been close and never related to one another on any level at all. Caught in the act, my mother knew the game was up. She furiously threw herself at Theodore attempting to strike him. He ducked and she lost her footing, falling face forwards onto the floor, screaming hysterically. Petrified, I yelled at Theodore.

"Leave her alone, can't you see she's hurt?"

"She will recover from the fall but not from the alcohol", intervened my grandmother in a detached, cold and imperious manner. "Sian, go and sleep in my bed tonight. I'll stay here with your mother. When she sobers up we will need to talk about a few things".

Theodore attempted to remonstrate with her but my grandmother retorted firmly:

"Theodore that's enough! Sian, go to bed and you go too. NOW." We both left the room like naughty boarders caught pillow fighting in an Enid Blyton school story. I remembered thinking that Theodore looked ridiculous in his red striped pyjama and flailing slippers that deposited white fluff over the cheaply carpeted floor.

I didn't sleep well that night as I could hear the distant hum of voices and the odd sob from my mother. Eventually, I fell into a restless sleep.

The next day Dr Klein was called and he arranged for my mother's admittance to a sanatorium twenty-five miles away where she would be treated for depression and alcoholism. After six weeks she was discharged and then immediately admitted to Foistneth Mental Hospital (known locally as 'the Looney Bin') for treatment. She did not return from there for five months and during this period she only had two weekends at home. My grandmother and I visited her every week at the gloomy mental hospital in Foistneth with restrictive visiting hours and bile-coloured walls. When I saw my mother for the first time after two and a half months, I hardly recognised her. She had lost weight and had aged considerably. She was quite calm (very unlike her) and she tended to stare a lot into space. I don't really think she had a clue what my grandmother and I were wrangling about in front of her - bus timetables I think it was.

"Well Sian", she said, "how is life treating you"?

This phraseology was most uncharacteristic of my mother but eight sessions of ECT might have been responsible for her ostensible change of personality. The doctors were pleased with her progress but were reluctant to discharge her because of her potential to relapse with alcohol. She was on a lot of medication and the clinicians believed she could be at risk of overdose if she drank alcohol with her current prescription. They expressed their concern about her ways of manipulating her family and secretively obtaining alcohol at home.

Theodore, unbeknown to any of us at the time, had struck up a liaison of sorts with Mattie the Mattress and he resented spending his Saturday afternoons sitting in a mental hospital listening to the ramblings of the deranged when the delights of Mattie's bed awaited him. He was so irritable that eventually my grandmother banned him from coming with us. I wasn't sorry either. On our return journey from the hospital, we usually went to Wilf's caff for a cup of tea and an Eccles cake. Whilst my grandmother discussed her daughter's progress with Wilf and Dora -or rather they asked intrusive questions and she fielded them, I sneaked into the back of the caff to find Pearl and entertain her with tales about 'the maddies' in the asylum. I was a good mimic and very able to imitate different accents as well as male and female voices. But I never discussed my mother because right down inside of me, it was too overwhelmingly painful to bear, let alone talk about.

"Oh, never mind luv!" said Dora to my grandmother, slapping yet more hot water onto the stewed tea leaves in the oversized metal teapot. The Jones' would be closing the cafe shortly and she didn't want to waste fresh tea on my grandmother.

"She's not the only one in Gwallgofedy. Do you remember Annie? The doctors said - 'Annie' they said, 'you will never get any better'. Oh, her daughter was horrified the way she was treated. Annie went funny and died there you know".

"Putt..." growled Wilf, "putt... putt... that's cheerful woman! Who needs a bad omen when you are around? Annie was a very different case. She was senile and was ill for years. Goddam putt... putt... Annie was in her seventies!"

"Don't be so soft, she wasn't as old as that!", retorted Dora sharply. "She looked seventy though. Anyway, she went funny didn't she? It must be awful for you luv", she turned consolingly to my grandmother who despised Dora as much as local shopkeepers despised Dean. Meanwhile, the jukebox in the corner played the last moving notes of 'I can't stop loving you' by Ray Charles. It had been chosen by a customer who had just left the café in a hurry to catch a bus. My grandmother was now alone in the café with the Jones'.

"This Eccles cake is stale, Dora", stated my grandmother, glaring at the cake and crumbling it with some distaste.

"Oh no luv, they are all fresh, we had a delivery yesterday".

"Well, they delivered you stale cakes yesterday, Dora. I don't want to pay for something that's stale. This tea is cold too.

"Putt" said Wilf... "putt. We'll give you another cake on this occasion, Mrs Thomas, but we won't make a habit of it you know. We know things aren't so easy for you at the present time like... putt.. putt".

My grandmother asked Dora to fetch me from the living quarters where I had gone behind the beaded curtain to see Pearl. This she duly did, interrupting a significant giggling session over an incident that had happened in the shop some weeks earlier. Dean was in the back kitchen too and he had initiated the fun by saying that 'Mr Williams Backstreet' had marched into the shop slamming a half pound of butter on the counter in front of Dora.

"This is the second time you have sold me rancid butter. I can't afford to waste my money like this. You are criminals - that's what you are!"

Dora had calmly tasted the butter.

"I can't taste anything wrong with it, luv. You probably kept it on the window in the sun. Butter will go off if it isn't kept on a cold slab in a pantry".

"It's March woman, where's the sun to melt the butter? I've got a refrigerator anyway. That butter's off and I want my money back!"

At this point Wilf tore out from the living quarters into cafe area. He thundered that he had done Williams Backstreet a favour by selling him the butter after five o'clock when all the other shops were closed. The butter was for their catering business so he needn't have sold it to Williams but he did so out of the goodness of his heart. So infused with rage was Wilf that he physically ejected the protesting Williams into the street for his perceived insult to Dora but not before Backstreet had informed the neighbourhood that he intended telling the police that the Jones' were selling 'stinker-bum butter'.

"Don't go in that cafe!" yelled a departing Williams Backstreet , "they cheat you. The tea is stale and they give you stinker-bum butter on your bread!"

He addressed Wilf as he retreated backwards down the street with Wilf 'putting' menacingly on the doorstep of his cafe.

"And get your bloody Persian cat off the sherbet lemons!", Williams Backstreet roared. "It's fur sticks to the sweets and causes the kids to bloody choke to death. People are complaining - I'll get the food inspector on you two, see if I don't. You are criminals that's what you are!"

Dean was enjoying the role-play, hollering raucously like a street vendor.

"Roll up! Stinker-bum butter - two and six a pound and only tuppence a bag for Sherbet Lemon Cats fur. Special offer. Roll up!"

Pearl and I were clutching our sides with laughter Pearl when Dora burst in, unamused by what she had just seen and heard. She castigated all three of us but she looked menacingly only at myself and her daughter.

"Come on Sian", she said impatiently, "your grandmother wants to go now or you'll miss the bus."

I said goodbye to Pearl and Dean, still giggling and hiccupping. Dora hissed as we went through the beaded curtain:

"You wanna be careful Sian, or you might end up on the funny farm like your mother!"

I ignored her remark but it cut me to the quick. I was silent on my bus journey home. Yes, my mother was 'on the funny farm' and people were talking about us behind our backs. Fortunately for me, the nastiest children on the school bus had left school at fifteen and many of the younger ones did not know my family well. Some parents feared my grandmother's wrath and reluctantly held their tongues when their offspring were around. On the journey home from Foistneth that evening, my grandmother occasionally remarked on my silence but I fobbed her off with some trivial excuse. I knew I would cause her distress and anger if I mentioned Dora's spiteful parting remark to me. She would never have dared to say anything like that to my grandmother. But maybe Dora was right. I could end up going the same way as my mother. The conversation with Dr Klein some years ago about giving my mother 'love and support' flashed into my mind. I remembered the talk in his kitchen and the distraction of Laurence's antics in the living-room that had caused me to have a giggling fit. What did 'love and support' mean outside of the context of teenage crushes and sexual longing?

It occurred to me that evening that I knew very little about life and what I did know came from my schoolwork and my avid reading of novels. I loved the fantasy world to which I could flee when loved ones were constantly haranguing or cruel to one another. In my fantasy world, people had rows and some individuals were disagreeable, spiteful and hypocritical but others were wise, thoughtful and loving as portrayed in the 'goody two-shoes' characters of a Charles Dickens or Charlotte Bronte novel. But I found it very difficult to handle ambiguity in fiction so a good gesture from a 'bad' character made me feel baffled and full of self-doubt. I wanted rules to attach my inner being to; I needed clarity. Good people would be rewarded (on this earth rather than in the next - in spite of what the Baptist minister said) and bad people would pay the price for their transgressions by becoming rejected by their former friends, suffering poverty and hardship. But part of me knew life wasn't that simple and that I had a lot to learn which I would never learn here. I swore to myself as I pressed my warm face against the misty window of the Western Welsh bus - nicknamed 'Wales Fargo' by Anna after a popular American television programme about a stagecoach company called 'Wells Fargo' - that I would leave this place in a year or two. If I did not - then I would have a breakdown and go mad - just like my mother. At the front of the bus, a pretty blonde girl was being cuddled by a young, beery soldier. They could hardly keep their hands off one another. My grandmother clucked disapprovingly about 'cheap girls and anti-social behaviour'. I scarcely noticed. What was ahead of me? Not a Rhett Butler or Cary Grant for sure. A soldier from the local barracks who needed God knows how many pints of beer before he could ask me to dance; maybe tea in a Foistneth caff and a ride home on Wales Fargo. No. Never! In American films, teenagers went out in a group, girls and boys, and the girls wore pretty dresses without cardigans and raincoats. Their white stilettos gleamed, un-streaked by persistent depressing drizzle and the muddy roads of South Wales. Of course, the Hollywood wardrobe department would have ensured the actors looked good in the Californian sunshine but at sixteen, my imagination didn't quite stretch to practicalities and cynicism. All I knew was that people in America were prone to smiling and saying how they felt about things. Here they sat in gloomy silence and criticised anyone who laughed. Local gossip drew people closer and provided some sort of emotional catharsis - giving individuals permission to express their anger, sadness, pain and personal prejudices through the 'safe' channel of the misfortunes of others. I knew then as I sat on the last bus from Foistneth that evening, that I would find it very hard to cope at home without the close bond of friendship with Pearl Jones and Anna Klein and I toyed with the idea of leaving South Wales forever. I knew there was 'life out there' where people could feel free to experience things their way without being attacked, dominated and crushed. It would be a struggle to fit into a different world but if I did not try then the result would be the village, Foistneth and Wales Fargo for the rest of my life; this price I knew then

I was never prepared to pay and dramatically told myself that I would rather die than continue daily existence in the drudgery of Foistneth. I glanced at the sculpted bone structure of my grandmother's beautiful face and her streaked grey bun - not unlike Miss Doody's, but not quite as large. My grandmother was not a happy woman; financial struggles and life disappointments had taken their toll on her physical appearance and personality but she possessed an indomitable spirit which I hoped I had inherited. People were wary of my grandmother because she spoke her mind and she had little time for gossip or sentimentality. At times she was harsh - for example towards her own daughter - but I think some of the bitterness was really frustration with herself and her disappointment in her marriage, her children and her social circumstances. Uncle Theodore was a miser, too selfish to be of any comfort to his mother. He was reluctant to seek accommodation elsewhere which would have cost him money and for her part, my grandmother needed the extra income to run the home so they tolerated each other for the sake of mutual convenience. Alice had spent every penny she could on alcohol and she had always been my grandfather's favourite and my grandmother's burden. My grandmother cared most about me and even if she never showed her feelings openly and rarely hugged me, I knew she cared. I resolved that evening, as I sketched a rising sun on the misted window of the 'Wales Fargo' bus, that as soon as I had finished my 'O' Levels I would leave Wales for good. I did leave eventually but not for another two very eventful years.

Chapter 5

Music: *'Apache'*: The Shadows, (1960)

One Saturday in mid-January I decided to visit my mother at the mental hospital in Foistneth but for once without my grandmother. This was not due to any altruistic motive on my part, but to a particular situation. I was staying the weekend with Pearl and we both agreed that the best way of getting away from Dora's 'elping in the caff' routine was to find an authentic reason for escape on a Saturday afternoon but without Dean in tow. Secretly we wanted to go to the Pavilion and see 'A Summer Place' which boasted an 'X' Certificate, meaning no admittance to under sixteens. Both of us were only a few months off the golden age of sixteen so Pearl and I reckoned that with make-up and a suspender belt to secure our 15 denier nylons we would gain admittance to the film. The matinee showing of the film was at 2 p.m. so we persuaded Wilf and Dora to let us go at one-thirty saying that Gwallgofedy visiting times were earlier on Saturdays. Wilf stated categorically that Dean was to stay as he would 'cause them all to go mad there'. Wilf had spoken, so Dora reluctantly complied even though Dean lay on his back like a sprayed fly, kicking out at her legs in a fit of rage. He sprawled directly in front of the door between the living quarters and the shop so Dora was forced to jump over his legs every time she attempted to serve a customer.

"Stop it Dean!", she shouted raucously. "I'll get the policeman... Wilf, look what he is doing now!"

Trembling lest Dora might persuade Wilf to change his mind, we made a fast exit up the High Street, in the direction of the Pavilion cinema. The suspender belts didn't work on this occasion and we were told to go to the Coliseum where they were showing 'The Swiss Family Robinson'. We were devastated as we adored the leading actor in the film, Troy Donahue. Just then, two boys appeared whom Pearl knew by sight. They were a couple of years older than us and seeing us dejectedly standing outside the cinema, told us not to worry as they would get tickets for us. They suggested we all sneak into the cinema when the cashier was busy elsewhere. Whilst we were scaping the coins out of our pockets to repay them, they then nonchalantly informed us that we could buy them both an ice-cream for their pains. We agreed. Troy was certainly worth the price of an ice. Everything went to plan and we entered the auditorium, the boys choosing seats in the back row, positioning themselves between Pearl and myself. The two boys were called Brian and Clive. We were barely a couple of clips into the Lyons Maid commercial when Brian's hand shot up my skirt and he began to teasingly caress the top of my leg. I sat still, frozen with disbelief. He must have thought I was enjoying the experience as he kept moving up my leg until he reached my suspender belt. Now he began to fumble hard and breathe deeply. Pushing his hand away didn't appear to work and I felt overwhelming shame as I didn't believe Pearl was suffering the same degradation from Clive. He appeared to be sitting calmly, intent on the screen. I felt both rage and humiliation because I didn't know how to react in a situation such as this. At school, you focus on all sorts of academic trivia - so dear to teachers - such as: 'Who said "Dr Livingstone, I presume?"' Surely, it would have been more meaningful to learn: 'How do you tell a young man you don't know, but who has just done you a favour, to get his hands out of your knickers without embarrassing yourself in front of a whole Pavilion full of teenagers?' We are expected to learn social rules from our parents but what if they don't know what the rules are or are too emotionally inhibited to tell you? Neither teachers nor parents told us how to cope in 'real life' situations. As Brian's hand slid determinedly along the side of my knickers, I began to panic, in the same instance livid at his intrusion because I wanted to watch the film so much. Tears of disappointment sprang to my eyes, then suddenly, I was galvanized into action. I leapt up and pushed past Clive and Pearl muttering that I needed to go to the toilet. I rushed to the lighted curtained exit next to the toilets but positioned myself behind the curtain so I could peep through the side, so as not to miss the feature film. I stayed there for about ten minutes before returning to the row where we were sitting and found a vacant seat to the left side of Pearl. She looked surprised and whispered something to me and I whispered back "tell you later". I watched the rest of the feature film in peace but I found the nerve to refuse to buy Brian an ice-cream saying I didn't have enough money.

In the short interval before the main film, he left us to torment another young girl in the front stalls. Clive invited Pearl out but she refused as she was dating a boy at the time. Many years later Brian served time in prison for rape but Clive ran a successful removals business based in Monmouth. At least on this occasion, the conclusion to reach is that life's rich tapestry is not wholly devoid of early warning signals. With the haunting score of 'A Summer Place' ringing in our ears, we caught one of the town buses to the mental hospital situated on the outskirts of Foistneth. The film had given us a false confidence and we believed our newly discovered social ease was responsible for our admittance to the hospital but it may have had more to do with the shortage of hospital staff on late Saturday afternoons.

My mother was sitting in the drab sitting-room with bile-green wallpaper, a perfect match for the bile-green corridor walls. She had a male visitor, sitting in a low chair in front of her and holding her hand in his. As we advanced she looked up suddenly and gasped, her hand to her mouth. She looked terrified.

"Sh..sh. Sian", she said, "this is Sian". The man, who was medium height, thin and very tanned suddenly smiled and held out his hand.

"You've grown a lot since I last saw you Sian, you are quite the young lady". I looked at him puzzled, Pearl hanging behind.

"You don't recognise me do you?", he said in a slight Irish accent, "I am your father". The sudden appearance of my father left me feeling shocked and dazed. I didn't know how to respond to him so I remember saying something inane like:

"It is nice to see you again, Dad."

My mother's excitement bothered me because I feared his visit might de-stabilise her and cause problems for my grandmother. I anticipated the furore when my grandmother eventually learned of his visit and what she would say and do to my mother. My father appealed to both of us not to mention a word to my grandmother. I knew I could trust Pearl as she of all people knew the consequences of disclosing anything in confidence to both her own mother and to Dean. Both would swear on God's existence, dead ancestors and their own lives that they would never tell. Within minutes of knowing the secret, they would blurt it out to all and sundry. As there was no evidence of repercussions from the Almighty, Dean and Dora continued to take religious oaths about keeping confidences and Pearl had long ceased to tell her mother anything of importance. I was greatly troubled by the thought of my grandmother's reaction and it continued to fill me with apprehension. My father suggested we meet him at the hospital again in a couple of weeks and he would take us to a pub. I said I would but deep down I knew I wouldn't because I did not want to deceive my grandmother. I believed his actions were wrong although I do remember thinking that it was up to my mother to decide what *she* wanted to do, not my grandmother.

I never saw my father at the hospital again or indeed anywhere else again over my whole life. I learned from my mother that he visited twice more. My grandmother found out some months later after my mother experienced another episode of deep depression when he didn't show up or give any explanation for not visiting. One of the nurses informed her of my father's clandestine visits. She became livid with rage when she learned she had not been told and insisted on talking to the doctor in charge of her daughter's case. She was slating to the point of rudeness with both the male consultant psychiatrist and the 'hoity-toity' matron. Neither succeeded in either placating or intimidating her. But one thing was certain, the hospital's brush with my implacable grandmother contributed favourably to the quality of my mother's care over the preceding months.

My grandmother did not suspect that I knew anything about my father's visit and I quaked lest she should find out from my mother who was not averse to landing me in it. However, my mother kept her counsel on this occasion. My grandmother was convinced that my father had shown up in order to get money out of us. She said she firmly believed that 'the land' was the real reason for his visit - not compassion for my mother. He knew the piece of land purchased at a discount from Sir Raoul Fenton many years ago had been divided equally between my mother and Theodore on their father's death and it had increased substantially in value over the years because of intransigent building regulations in the National Park area within the district of Foistneth. My grandmother was adamant that my father was cooking up some half-baked scheme to get my mother's share from her. She said he would easily get his tentacles around Alice who was naive and dependent on others for approval. I felt I would never forgive my father for the second round of unwarranted distress he caused my mother but this time it was not my grandmother who forced him to abruptly end contact. He inexplicably gave my mother no reason for his decision to suddenly disappear again. His visits set her back emotionally and destroyed the little confidence that she was beginning to acquire. I was then glad for her sake that she was in the mental hospital getting help rather than at home being constantly criticised by Theodore and my grandmother. Many years later she told me how devastated she was when my father stopped visiting but she saw him then for what he really was. She told me that she learned to accept that he did not love her and would never return to her, ever. I do not quite remember it like that but memory can play us false sometimes, especially after so many years. All I recall was a time of discomfort, insecurity, fear and great confusion.

Our sixteenth year was the last year we three would spend together in South Wales. We would meet again for days or weeks at any one time, sometimes as a twosome, other times as a threesome but the bond of our shared childhood experiences effectively ended that summer. Throughout August of that year, the weather had been even wetter and greyer than usual in spite of our desperate prayers to the Almighty for a fine day for the Foistneth fair. The fair was held in the local park every year. In retrospect, I remember most August fairs as sunny and sparklingly colourful but I wonder whether this was a trick of the imagination, blending the Californian carousels of Hollywood into the drab and wet annual events of Foistneth. On this particular day, the sky hung heavy with cloud. A persistent drizzle flattened and frizzled our backcombed hair and our white stiletto heels gained stripes of brown mud with every step we took. Anna and I had caught the village bus together, planning to meet Pearl at the fair. We were excited because we felt 'real teenagers' with our buzzing hormones, 15 denier nylon stockings and powdered faces. Anna had sneaked out an old lipstick of her mother's and we applied it, somewhat unevenly, to our lips during the monotonous bus ride to Foistneth. The Kleins had not been told of our intentions to go to the fair as Saturday was a religious day but we felt less remorseful thinking that Anna would soon be leaving our area and we needed to do one last thing together before she moved altogether. We all unanimously agreed that Anna could conform to Jewishness full time in Cardiff.

Pearl was waiting by the dodgems as arranged. She too, had avoided telling her parents that she had taken the day off her Saturday job because Dean would have insisted on coming with her. Anna's parents fortunately decided against going to synagogue on that particular weekend as they were preparing for their imminent move to Cardiff, a move that all three of us dreaded as we believed we had little chance of ever meeting up again. Wilf had a car but he only drove within a ten-mile radius of Foistneth. He also drove so slowly that one local maintained that a magpie built a nest on the roof of Wilf's car when he was driving back from a village just six miles away. It was a standing joke among farmers at the local market that any tractor could go faster than Wilf Jones driving in the rain and he never overtook any vehicle larger than a bicycle There was precious little chance of his driving Pearl and myself to Cardiff to visit Anna. We did not own a car but I knew that even if Theodore eventually passed his driving test, he would refuse to drive us anywhere as he was far too tight-fisted.

Pearl had taken a Saturday job at a local sports shop earn some money for clothes as her parents were stingy with her pocket money. Dora continued to take Pearl for granted when it came to 'elping' in the shop so Pearl's decision to work a Saturday job gave her freedom from both the café and Dean as well as the means to purchase things beyond her tight budget. Both Wilf and Dora had little respect for education believing it was a waste of time and only 'the brainy' and 'them nobs' were absolved from criticism for undertaking it. They sneered at anyone not conforming to these two groups. 'The brainy' needed something different to do from 'the likes of we' and 'nobs' were to be respected for their class and eccentricity. They were particularly vitriolic if education aspiring individuals were from working class backgrounds:

"Who does she think she is? Her father was only a bus driver! You remember Len Owens driving the buses? His poor sister had a baby by a soldier - but Len always had plenty of edge on nothing - mind you! His daughter is just like him".

The three of us 'fancied' local Grammar School boys and hoped to catch a glimpse of them at the fair. The persistent drizzle was annoying as it ruined our hairdos as well as our chances. Pearl dashed some of Mrs Klein's 'cherry harmony' across her lips. She was the only one who had left home dressed conventionally in a cotton skirt and white blouse as she was meant to be going to work. Anna and I wore hoops, attached tightly to a stiff petticoat, under our short floral dresses and white stiletto-heeled shoes. Anna always left her hoop at my house as Mrs Klein did not approve. We felt groovy and hopeful of catching the eye of the opposite sex. After some debate, we decided to ride on the dodgems and the three of us tried to crowd into one car. Two unruly dress hoops would not allow this and we ended up trying to re-arrange them whilst arguing. Pearl said that when we sat down our knickers were on display. The dodgem car assistant stood impassively by, taking it all in. He was well aware of just how many girls admired his slim, lithe figure and enigmatic look beneath his dark sunglasses. He was so different from the self-conscious young men of our acquaintance as there was something wild and gypsy-ish about him. He persuaded Pearl to move to an adjoining car containing a young girl aged about twelve. Her name was Enid Morgan and it was her first year at our Grammar School. Anna whispered that the dodgem man reminded her of Heathcliff in 'Wuthering Heights'. 'Heathcliff' spent most of the ride hanging on the back of Pearl and Enid's dodgem. Anna and I shouted loudly to each other above the whining engines of the cars struggling for ascendency over an amplified version of Del Shannon's 'Runaway'. We kept score of the number of times 'dodgem man' rode on the back of our car compared to Pearl's. Pearl had double the number of visits by 'Heathcliff' and we teased her about it afterwards. I was jolted by the deliberate crashing of some of the cars into us and had to overcome my dread of injury during the ride. Whilst steering, I tried hard to avoid bumping into other cars with their flashing overhead mechanisms attached to a long metal pole. Nevertheless, the excited Foistneth lads had every intention of hurtling their cars into ours but they didn't dare take advantage when 'Heathcliff' stood confidently on the back of our car. It was difficult manoeuvring the car with a hoop stuck out in front of me because I had to lean over it in order to manipulate the steering wheel. Anna criticised my driving continually until I shouted at her to shut up. She sulked for a while but forgot the insult later during a competition requiring an accurate aim of a plastic ping-pong ball into a narrow-necked goldfish bowl. Pearl said Dean had flushed her last goldfish down the toilet so if she won she would make a present of her goldfish to one of us for its own protection. That proved to be unnecessary as none of us had a good enough aim to win a goldfish anyway. We also tried our luck at competing for a large teddy-bear at the rifle range. Although I did the best out of the three of us, only three out of the six metal ducks required for the coveted teddy were knocked flat by our shared rifle. Dejected, we loitered around, searching for the teenage male talent of the day that so far had been successful at eluding us. We ran into some boys we knew from school and they launched into an animated description about some dangerous ride they had just attempted. During this conversation, Pearl suddenly gave a strangled gasp, turning her back on us and quickly sped out of sight - disappearing between the flapping canvas edge of the rifle range to the right of us and a temporarily vacant sweet stall. I watched her fast-departing figure in amazement until I realised what the problem was: Dean was heading towards us with a friend of his. I knew Pearl would get into a lot of trouble for lying if Dean caught sight of her. Anna opened her umbrella to shield us from his view but I expected him to descend on us any second. He did not. He was intent on talking to his companion and they veered off in another direction ignoring us trembling beneath the umbrella but I was determined to lie about Pearl's whereabouts if questioned by Dean.

Inexplicably, our male acquaintances suddenly dumped us for a more exciting pastime, another ride on 'The Bomb' which people said was a ride far too dangerous for under eighteens to undertake and that some people never recovered from the shock of the experience. Naturally this news attracted all young people under the age of eighteen. An impassive man at the ticket counter repeated monotonously to each person purchasing a ticket and whose age might be in doubt and indeed in some cases where age was indisputable:

"Over eighteen?"

Whereupon each person answered emphatically "last birthday" or simply "yes". It was evident that some of the kids queuing were nowhere near the mandatory age as their height reached all of four feet. But the flat tone continued:

"Over eighteen?"

Sometimes, the ritual caused comment and laughter. One woman was heard to exclaim: "Well if that hasn't made my day, Dewi, us with grandkids and all!"

'The Bomb' had two oval carriages at either end of a swinging metal contraption that swept forwards and backwards and around in an arc. As its speed increased, it swung off the ground and into the air with fast gaining velocity, turning itself upside down with people screaming in terror and hanging on for their lives. When it stopped, one carriage remained at ground level whilst the other remained capsized in the air. Riders would groan and plead to be let off and horror stories abounded about how people had died as 'the blood rushed to their heads driving them mad'. But these anecdotes obviously did not deter our enthusiastic male companions. Pearl had disappeared down the side of the stall with the wide awning and Anna and I right away decided to look for her. After wasting a good twenty minutes searching, we gave up and returned to the more enjoyable distractions of the fair. We kept telling each other that Pearl had gone home. Foistneth's park was large and it housed an outdoor swimming pool, tennis courts, a cricket pitch and a children's playground. We moved towards the tennis courts at the back entrance to the park, partly to look for Pearl and partly to find somewhere to sit. The drizzle had stopped temporarily but we looked frights. Anna's hair had lost its bouffant look and was now frizzled to tight unfashionable curls by the relentless rain. My white shoes were filthy from the mud and my bouffant had long become as flat as Miss Doody's bun. Both of us had managed to ladder our nylons and we looked and felt ill at ease with our unruly hoops, our feet aching from tottering so long in alien high heels. The discomfort experienced so far had been for nothing as we had seen neither of the boys we so desired. The excruciatingly loud music and raucous whirr and hum of the rides had given Anna a headache. We had already spent almost all of our money and I felt sick from the sugary blend of toffee-apples and candy floss I had devoured in the space of half an hour and believed I would throw up on the bus. We found an unoccupied and semi-dry bench under a tree near the stream that ran diagonally across from the tennis courts. There were tall elm trees at the edge of the park screening a line of council houses from view. "Sian, Anna!" a voice called from behind one of the elms. Pearl was hiding there and beckoning to us. She looked very scared. Her knee was bleeding and her hair was sticking up as if she had been struck by lightning. I vaguely remember thinking how exaggerated her behaviour was. Wilf had never hit his daughter and although Dora was spiteful and would punish Pearl by withdrawal of privileges, she was also equally likely to be distracted by the opportunity of a good boast so the punishment would not be upheld for long.

"Pearl!" cried Anna, "Oh thank goodness we have found you! Listen, I don't think Dean saw you, he.."

"Oh, bugger Dean!", retorted Pearl, in a most unfamiliar way, "I don't care whether he saw me or not. No, I'm really worried about Enid - Enid Morgan." She burst into tears. "Something really bad has happened."

"What is it?" I asked, dumbfounded by the turn of events. Trembling with emotion, Pearl told us her story. She had run off across the fields at the back of the stalls after spotting Dean and his companion. She ran as hard as she could without pausing for breath. Realising she would need to go home or bump into Dean if she stayed in the confines of the fairground, she worked out her options and eventually decided to find the back exit and get away as fast as possible. She forced open a gate, only to find herself in a field of curious cows that advanced towards her in convoy. Terrified, Pearl broke into a run but the over-milked and thoroughly bored animals gave chase, delighted by the novel entertainment. Pearl reached the furthest corner of the field and seeing the cows hot on her trail, pushed herself through a balding part of a spindly hedge, only just managing to escape her determined pursuers. She hurt her knee on the thorny hedge and it tore her skin to bleeding as she escaped into the next field. Bits of hedge still clung to her hair. Crying from the sharp stabbing pain caused by the thorns, she managed to get up, scream abuse at the cows from the safety of the other side and make her way back along a tiny lane. Pearl believed she was aiming back towards the park but in fact she was heading in the opposite direction. The lane ran out suddenly, widening into a small coppice that she had never seen before. She found herself standing on a low incline and in the distance she could hear the muffled music from the fair. Pearl then realised that she would need to retrace her footsteps in the opposite direction but briefly stopped to observe with dismay the state of her shredded nylon stockings. She was about to set off again when she heard what sounded like sobbing.

"Please", a young girl's voice pleaded, "please stop, please".

Pearl cautiously crept into the coppice keeping herself hidden from view as she tried to discover the origin of the voice. I often thought that our old 'stalking the villain' techniques when role-playing Enid Blyton's Famous Five contributed to her expert handling of the situation. She hid behind a thick, prickly bush and from this position was able to view the scene. She gasped when she saw young Enid Morgan lying on the damp ground, her unmistakable long white-blond hair spread out like a sheet behind her. A wide overweight man lay straddled over her, his legs apart, encompassing her thin body. Pearl did not recognise him as she saw only the back of his bulky cropped head but said later that his profile was vaguely familiar. Pearl realised was that he was hurting Enid who was begging him to stop, weakly shouting for her mother. Enid was desperately in need of help. Pearl fought herself to go to Enid's aid as her immediate thought was to run away. In a voice shaking with trepidation, Pearl took a deep breath and called out in a resolute voice:

"E....nid.... where are you?"

The man leaped up - tearing at his trousers in folds below his knees. Pearl said with some embarrassment: "I saw his willy when he pulled them up". He shouted 'fuck' as he stood up. I screamed: 'run Enid!' but I did not stop to check whether she had or not - I was too frightened. I tore off down the lane in the direction of the park. I didn't even bother to check whether Enid was following. I was terrified the man had seen me and that he would attack me as well."

How she found her way from the lane to a quiet road of council houses leading to the back entrance of the park she never knew - all she knew was that she was petrified. She hid under a laurel bush for a while and then edged her way behind a tree opposite waiting for enough time to pass so that she could go home safely when she recognised Anna and myself sitting on a bench. The three of us then debated what to do, knowing that any decision spelled trouble. Pearl had run away and left Enid to her tormentor. We would need to inform the police and they would criticise Pearl's unwillingness to help Enid as Enid Blyton's heroines would have done. Enid Morgan may have escaped but we didn't really know whether she had. We didn't even know where the police station was but Pearl suddenly remembered. There was a dilemma: informing the police meant disclosing that Pearl and Anna, both without parental permission, were at the fair and that Pearl was running to hide from her own brother. Oh God, Dora's face! Pearl said she could never disclose that. The other option was to take a chance on it and tell no one, hoping Enid had escaped. Anna was against this plan more than Pearl and me, saying that we could not live with such a deed on our conscience and it was better to own up to our parents now. Reluctantly, we trailed away in the direction of the fair, intending to give one last look around to see if Enid had returned there. The police station was in the same direction. As we moved through the central part of the fairground, heading towards the main gate, Pearl was openly defiant about encountering Dean whose presence had now become insignificant within the wider scale of escalating events. We were almost at the gate when we saw Dr Klein advancing towards us, waving his umbrella and shouting at his daughter:

"Where haf you bin on Shabbos?"

When angry, Dr Klein's English sounded more like German. Anna burst into tears but she said nothing. I became angry. It occurred to me that our problems were indirectly caused by the adults in our lives and that they should be aware of how their actions sometimes made our life intolerable. I held my head high and coldly and firmly told Dr Klein about Enid's attack witnessed by Pearl and how we were off to the police station to report it. Dr Klein listened as I had a feeling he would. He insisted that we return to the fairground as there were always police somewhere on site and it would be better not to lose any more time. We eventually found the police trailer. They listened to Dr Klein and then called many times over the megaphone:

"Would Miss Enid Morgan please report to the police trailer. Miss Enid Morgan, please report to the police trailer."

We waited for about twenty minutes and were about to leave when Enid showed up with a couple of adults that appeared to be her aunt and uncle. I glanced at Pearl who had turned ashen when suddenly confronted by the adults. The man laughed when the police related how Pearl had witnessed Enid being attacked.

"She was with us all afternoon. The little bitch is lying."

The man smelled of beer and his mood was aggressive. His nervous little wife kept apologising, saying it must have been her fault but her niece would have told her if she had been attacked. Enid said nothing and kept her eyes on the ground. Her hair was in disarray, streaked as it was with dirt and leaves. Her aggressive uncle shouted at her:

"For the love of Mike, you little idiot, tell the police the truth, you weren't attacked were you?".

At this point Dr Klein stepped forward and said calmly:

"Enid will discuss this with me at another time. I am her doctor and also her mother's doctor. Perhaps we should be more sensitive in front of so many people".

Enid's uncle, 'Black Rod' Bowen, was well known to the police for his drinking and brawls as well as for petty pilfering from the factory where he worked on an assembly line. The police were reluctant to let go of Black Rod but his wife kept bleating that Rod was upset by Pearl's story as it implied they were not looking after their niece properly. Black Rod's widowed sister-in-law, Enid's mother, was a nervous, gentle woman with prematurely greying hair. She was not unlike Rod's wife, in character. The police 'warned' Rod but no one was clear as to what he was being warned about. The Bowens then went on their way and as they passed us, we could smell his beery breath and see his baggy bloodshot eyes. He stopped and swayed in front of Pearl.

"Did you see the man that was supposed to have attacked our Enid?"

He stared full into Pearl's eyes and muttered something incomprehensible. After he disappeared from sight, Dr Klein began another conversation with the police and it was then that Pearl lurched forwards and grabbed her stomach as if in pain. Her face was contorted with fear.

"What is it Pearl, what is it?", I whispered anxiously.

I was concerned by her physical distress and white face. I thought she was about to pass out. She looked into my eyes and groaned hoarsely:

"It was him attacking Enid. It was him. He... he ... just threatened to kill me!"

Pearl had nightmares for years after this event, always about Black Rod attacking her and forcing himself onto her. Dr Klein spoke to Enid's mother and to her abusing brother-in-law who had raped the child many times before and terrorised her into silence. The case went to court and he was given a short prison sentence. He was banned from ever having any access to Enid again. Enid did not get justice but Black Rod Bowen got his comeuppance three years later. He had an accident with a forklift truck at work that provided him with a considerable compensation payment but left him paralysed from the waist down. He was no longer physically capable of sexually abusing children as he was confined to a wheelchair and dependent on his wife. But he was still verbally aggressive to her as she meekly pushed him around the village in his wheelchair. As he passed, local kids chased his wheelchair trying to get him to say 'fuck off you little bastards!' They traded insults with him and loudly mimicked the screeching sound of the wheelchair that alerted his arrival. He was a thoroughly dislikeable man whom no one felt sorry for. When he died, his wife inherited the compensation money although Bowen had managed to spend a considerable part of it on drink and gambling. Mrs Bowen continued to tell anyone who cared to listen what a good husband and father Black Rod had been. Many years later Pearl ran into Enid at the A & E department of a Northwest London hospital where Enid was working as a nurse. After exchanging pleasantries and wonderment at their casual meeting in such a vast city, Enid openly thanked Pearl for her intervention those many years ago. It had saved her from further pain and humiliation. We are often unaware of how much our actions indirectly influence the lives of others and this was a classic example. If Anna had stayed at home, Dr Klein would not have come to the fair and if Pearl had not lied and tried to avoid Dean, none of us would have been any the wiser concerning Enid's Morgan's persistent suffering. As for the three of us, we all matured in our different ways as a direct consequence of our experience that day at Foistneth Fair.

Chapter 6

Music: *'Please Me'*, The Beatles (1962)

Pearl left school at sixteen against the advice of her teachers who believed she had the academic ability for a university education. Wilf and Dora vilified the teachers behind their backs, adamant that Pearl would leave school and work locally as they had done. Pearl's principal problem was living at home, particularly with Dean around so she considered neither suggestion. She made the only choice she felt open to her at the time. After much soul searching, discussions with Anna and myself until the early hours and many sleepless nights, Pearl mentally rehearsed her speech to Wilf and Dora. She had opted to leave home and become an au pair to a professional family in London. The three of us had spent some time researching au pair posts outside of Wales and as far away from Dean as possible. Pearl wrote to four families advertising for an au pair in 'The Lady' magazine. She got a definite reply from one who asked to meet within the next two weeks. Pearl broke the news to her astounded parents. Wilf exploded with anger - the 'putts' trebling as he ruminated on her defiance and lack of gratitude to her parents. He phoned the London family that she had arranged to meet and threatened them with the local police officer. Wilf's anger was so out of control that for the first time in his life he came close to striking his daughter. Even Dora was fearful of his outbursts but then she suddenly changed tack, adopting the role of mediator, saying she could understand Pearl needing a change after studying so hard for her 'O' Levels.

"All that studyin's affected her 'ead Wilf, I told you so!".

For once Dean stayed out of the way, in the living quarters at the back of the shop, silently observing the boiling emotional temperature within his family. This was indeed a new role for Dean who was usually the cause of any domestic upheaval. But on this occasion, Pearl was the focus of parental indignation. Pale-faced and quivering with apprehension, she told Wilf in a flat tone that she **could** leave home at sixteen and that legally he could not keep her there against her will.

"Oh Pearl, you'll kill your father!" ventured Dora, dismayed by her daughter's open disobedience.

"Shut up woman! I'm trying to get to the bottom of things here. Keep your drama for the chapel."

Dora blanched, for one terrible moment she thought Wilf was referring to her dalliance with the deacon, rather than to the amateur dramatics group that staged tragedies in the chapel vestry once a year. With a trembling voice and very close to tears, Pearl said she needed to get away, if only for six months. The mention of 'six months' slightly mollified Wilf; it also made it easier for him to back down without losing face. He knew full well that his daughter was as stubborn and determined as he was and when she reached a decision, she would follow it through - no matter what. Dora suggested that if Pearl needed a break from Foistneth, Cardiff would be a good option as it is 'still in Wales' and perhaps she could stay for a while with 'the Jewess'. But the Jones' entrenched attitude towards their daughter began to shift slightly over the following weeks when they realised that she was single-minded with regard to her future employment and had no intention of changing her mind.

Pearl found employment as an au pair with a family in Oxfordshire as the original potential London employers were far too alarmed by Pearl's family to reconsider giving her a contract. Pearl's future employer, Thomas Mellor-Clarke, was described by the Jones' as 'a gentleman farmer' and according to Dora - capitalizing on the boast - 'the lady of the house was more 'la di dah than Lady Fenton'. The family had two children aged eighteen months and four years. Wilf wrested a commitment from Pearl that she would return home to Foistneth after six months if she was not happy. He uncharacteristically took the plunge and decided to drive Pearl to Banbury as he wanted to check out that the Mellor-Clarkes were not 'white slavers' - ready to ship Pearl out to the fleshpots of the Middle East. They left at 5 a.m. in the morning to avoid traffic in Foistneth but bearing in mind that this was 1962, in a small market town in a rural area where few people had cars, Wilf's precautions were somewhat exaggerated. Dean opted out of the travel experience as he rightly guessed what was in store. Pearl later told us about the horrific journey which sounded like a comedian's star turn on Blackpool pier. The Jones' kept losing their way but refused to take Pearl's map reading seriously in spite of her best efforts to direct them. Individuals asked for help along the way were treated to explanations about the reasons for Pearl leaving Wales and their urgent need to arrive in Banbury near Oxford. Many years later Pearl said that her journey to Oxfordshire reminded her of a scene from the comedy film 'Airplane' when the obsessive conversation of Elaine's husband concerning the break-up of their marriage, drives a despairing Hindu passenger sitting next to him to threaten suicide by setting himself alight. English passers-by were baffled by Wilf's detailed explanations for undertaking his trip to Banbury, wondering what it had to do with them. Eventually the Jones' arrived at the Mellor-Clarke's magnificent stone farmhouse, thanks to the patient directions of locals in awe of Jones' and knowledgeable van drivers. Wilf's presence in the local village sparked some reaction, especially when he rolled down his car window and waylaid a man in a deerstalker:

"Hey, Hicker! I'm looking for a gentleman farmer with a double barrel name and bit of a la di dah wife. See, our Pearl is going to work there as their au pair like..." The man looked confused and Dora leaned across her husband from the passenger seat shouting:

"The Mellor-Clarke's, luv. Do you know where the Mellor-Clarke's live?".

The Mellor-Clarke's farmhouse was set back from the road in ample acreage of farmland and within reasonable walking distance of the village where a chastened Pearl swore she would never go again as she could read the incredulity and laughter in the eyes of those asked for directions.

The Jones' duly arrived at their destination. Their compact little black Ford car pulled to a stop in the square courtyard in front of the main entrance to the farmhouse. Their arrival was heralded by a growling sheepdog and a yelping Jack Russell. Wilf was wary of dogs and was reluctant to get out of the car so Dora got out first and clouted the Jack Russell with her handbag when it attempted to jump up and mark her 'best skirt' with its muddy paws. Mrs Mellor-Clarke and the children came out to greet them and after the initial introductions, they were taken into the living-room and given tea. Dora was disappointed that the house was not as grand as it appeared from the outside and was surprised by the lack of carpets on the tiled floors. Also, Mrs Mellor-Clarke did not sound as 'lah di dah' as she had on the telephone (they were to learn later that they had in fact spoken to her mother-in-law, not to her). She was in her late twenties, a little on the plump side, with a fresh complexion and sandy hair drawn back in a plait. She wore glasses and spoke with a slight Oxfordshire burr. Her four-year old son James resembled her in appearance but her baby daughter Joanna was darker in colouring. Mrs Mellor-Clarke showed enough courtesy to her visitors but frowned when Dora lit up her umpteenth cigarette of the day and waved the smoke in her baby's face, causing her to splutter. Mr Mellor-Clarke was busy with his farm manager and returned barely fifteen minutes before the Jones' departed. He also brought with him another two enormous sheepdogs that growled menacingly at Wilf who began to 'putt..tt..' nervously about the long journey back to Wales. However, Mellor-Clarke was there long enough for Dora to classify him as 'a real nob' by his accent and bearing. Pearl heaved a sigh of relief when the little black Ford disappeared down the winding drive, obscuring her parents from view, but at the same time, she was apprehensive. She was sixteen years old and had never been out of Wales. The Jones' cafe business had stopped them from having any kind of family holiday together and Pearl had never stayed anywhere overnight apart from my own and Anna's homes in the near-by village. Hearing the distant hum of the engine of her parents' car as they headed for the main road, she felt a sudden tug of conscience because way down, at a visceral level, she knew from now on things would change and that she would not find it easy to adapt to the changes. She also knew that however much her parents infuriated her, she really loved them and knew she would miss them.

Pearl was not a prolific writer but she sent the occasional postcard and I believe I received two letters from her the year she left Foistneth. She stayed with the Mellor-Clarke's for just over two years and even spent a summer holiday with them in Italy. She always said she was glad she 'stuck it out' because she was solely tempted in the early days to return home as she felt so homesick for Foistneth, her family and her friends. The Mellor-Clarke's family relationships and interactions, linguistic structuring and vocabulary was so different from what Pearl was accustomed to. For example, 'table-napkins' and 'lavatory' were used in the place of 'serviette' and 'toilet' (definitely not Dora's 'lavi'!). 'I'm starving cold' was a common Foistneth saying,

denoting the severity of the cold but without hunger. In England 'starving' meant very hungry and was not related to the weather conditions. Pearl came up against these linguistic nuances a great deal in the early months of her stay in Oxfordshire as she struggled to adapt to her immediate environment. Fruit was served at breakfast with a knife and fork and the children were given fresh fruit juice, not 'pop', and sweets were rationed. Pearl was shy but she developed a friendly, if distant, relationship with Grace, Mrs Mellor-Clarke. Mr Mellor-Clarke was more of an enigma but once she became accustomed to what she perceived was his abrupt manner, she found him kind and obliging in many ways. The children were well-behaved overall and Grace was always on hand if one of them was ill or had hurt themselves. The family had an active social life and many of their friends came to visit at the farm but the Mellor-Clarkes rarely made overnight stays without taking their children with them. They encouraged Pearl to go to evening class and learn shorthand and typing as these pragmatic skills would give her more options for a future job. Pearl was not keen but she agreed, mainly to win approval from the Mellor-Clarkes but also to meet other people as she felt quite isolated on the farm with people who were a minimum of ten years older than her. She didn't fare much better at the evening shorthand and typing classes as few students were under twenty and the younger contingent were not particularly friendly. Pearl was socially inept and needed someone to draw her out. There was also the disadvantage that Thomas Mellor-Clarke collected her after the class to avoid her walking back in the dark as there was no late bus in walking distance of the farm. This meant she had to refuse any invitations to the pub after the class.

"It's worse than bloody Foistneth", thought Pearl despondently.

But as the nights drew in, things changed for Pearl. A young man called Jack from the creative writing class, running at the same time as the shorthand-typing class, approached Pearl in the coffee break and invited her out for a drink. She accepted and as he was in possession of a small and battered old Brake car, he was able to run her back to the farm afterwards. Pearl's social life began to take off. She went to dances with Jack and his 'coupled' friends. She told me in one of her letters that she liked Jack but did not love him enough 'to go all the way' with him. Also, like the rest of us, she was terrified of getting pregnant and ending up being gossiped about everywhere she went. Years of Dora's whispers behind the backs of passing girls haunted Pearl:

"I won't tell you everything luv, but she got pregnant by a married man last year and had the baby adopted - awful isn't it?"

Dora had taught Pearl to fear the shame of unwanted pregnancy above all other things. However, Pearl had been more attracted to other boys in the past than she currently was to Jack so she was determined all the more to stay a virgin. She said in her letter that if he put too much pressure on her she would be forced to end their relationship. Jack eventually left her for a more compliant girl but by that time Pearl was learning to drive with 'Thomas' and her social circle had begun to extend beyond the few people at evening classes and their immediate acquaintances. Pearl went to some rock concerts in Oxford and stayed over at the house of a woman distantly related to the Mellor-Clarkes. The woman's daughter was called Beth and she was still at school on her last year of A levels. Beth kept a supply of cannabis weed hidden in a sock in her underwear drawer and she and Pearl sometimes smoked out of the window of Beth's room or in the shed at the bottom of the garden. One night, Pearl ended up having sex with a student in the back of his car after

consuming a vast quantity of alcohol, neurologically enhanced by cannabis smoking. She said what she remembered most about that evening was the Beatles' music - 'Please, Please Me' that was being played at the disco. Over the following weeks, until her next period, Pearl lived in terror of finding herself pregnant. She had many sleepless nights and cut back on her social life. She was beginning to find the children too demanding with little James insisting she read the same story at least twice before he went to bed, sharply commenting if she skipped any pages. But Pearl was good with children; she had patience and was able to relate to a child's mind in such a way that she soon gained their confidence. Grace pointed this out to Pearl saying she would make an excellent nanny if she ever chose to make it a career. But Pearl was uncertain about any kind of career and certainly did not see herself as a nanny for the rest of her life.

The second letter I received from Pearl came after Christmas. I was bitterly disappointed she had decided to remain in Banbury for Christmas but she said the Mellor-Clarkes had a number of guests and asked her to stay over the Christmas period. She would be given a longer holiday later in the year. Part of me felt Pearl did not really want to come home for Christmas as she would be stranded in Foistneth and forced 'to 'elp' in the café. Pork pies, the vicious and smelly Persian cat (a present to Dora from the deacon) and Dean were not part of her new life anymore and she dreaded the dark, wet and dull Christmas days in Foistneth. Her last letter to me was jubilantly ecstatic:

"*Sian, thank God I am not pregnant! I went down on my knees and thanked God today. I will make sure something like this will never, ever happen again. I've been so worried.... I can't tell you. Oh, by the way, I've passed both my shorthand and typing exams. I've got a 'merit' pass for typing so I'm pretty pleased.*"

A good twelve months after this letter, Pearl found a job in an insurance broker's office in Oxford and shared a flat with a couple of overseas students. She didn't like the job and found her manager impatient and frequently rude to both staff and customers. She changed her job within months (most unlike Pearl) and went to work for a company called 'Flatfinders' that mainly found accommodation for students. Pearl loved the job and before her nineteenth birthday was offered a senior position in London on a considerably higher salary at Flatfinders' new office in Hampstead, Northwest London. Pearl had some misgivings, but she agreed realising that she needed to build up her confidence and move on. But there was a downside: she had lived in Oxfordshire for almost two and a half years, systematically developing a circle of friends and acquaintances. Now she would be starting all over again, alone in a big city. She accepted the challenge of the new job because she really wanted to do it and the extra money was very tempting. Talking of this years later, Pearl said she had been so naive about the astronomical cost of accommodation and transport in London compared to the rest of Britain and probably if she had been a little more 'switched on', it is unlikely that she would have gone to London at all. I am glad that she did because our friendship remained so solid due to the regular contact we retained there over many years. But my visit to her, whilst still at the Mellor-Clarkes, was by no means how I had imagined it.

In the summer of 1963, the year before my A. Level examinations, I found some seasonal work as a waitress in a pretentious county hotel called 'The Glaisfar'. It was summer when I first met Harold Stanton and the consequences of our chance meeting were to remain with me for the rest of my life. The hotel was about some four miles from my village and Theodore had reluctantly lent my grandmother the money to purchase a second-hand bicycle for me to cycle to work as the Glaisfar was in a remote area. There were few buses and it could only be reached comfortably by motorcar. I would cycle daily to my work through a private wood belonging to Sir Rob. The wood was always deserted when I travelled through it - which was not surprising as there were large wooden notices everywhere, declaring:

PRIVATE. FENTON ESTATE
KEEP OUT.
TRESPASSERS WILL BE PROSECUTED

Many locals like myself ignored Sir Rob's threats and claim to ownership. We enjoyed walking through the woods and picnicking at our favourite spots near the river. The distant hills rose majestically above the river landscape adding to its breath-taking beauty. One flat-topped and slightly lopsided hill bore the name of 'Table Mountain'. Numerous times the three of us had spent our summers picking wimberries on the Table Mountain but it was a hazardous place to reach. In one particular spot we literally had to follow a narrow track littered with jagged stones through a farmyard, the home of a very bad-tempered farmer. Once, he threatened us with a gun after a day's binge on home-made cider. But even the gun was preferable to Toss, the farmer's sly and particularly vicious dog who would stalk us lying almost flat on its belly in the grass. Then, the creature would suddenly leap erect, blocking our path like a wild animal about to pounce, with barred teeth and nerve-curdling growls. Toss had small, mean eyes and discoloured teeth. We were all terrified of the animal which is exactly what the sadistic farmer intended. He would yell impatiently:

"Here Toss!"

The creature would grudgingly leave its petrified prey and slink off with fading growls into the distance. We nicknamed Toss 'The Hound of the Baskervilles'. Once we three saw the film of the same name and when the hound appeared on screen for the first time, I could not resist the temptation to leap up and holler: "Here Toss!" - causing my friends to giggle uncontrollably. Angry 'shushes' were hurled at us from an enraged audience followed by the threat of eviction by a forceful cinema usherette.

As I cycled along the bridlepath in the direction of the Glaisfar Hotel, the only audible background sounds were the lapping and splashing of the River Usk on the rocks below and the rustling activity of game and wildlife in the trees and bushes long the path. A rabbit darted out from the undergrowth, narrowly missing the front wheels of my unpaid for bicycle. I braked and got off cursing aloud. I was startled by the appearance of a man advancing slowly towards me. He was a stranger carrying a map. I noted with some nervousness that I was within a mile or so of the hotel. I fervently hoped the man was not a murderer.

"Hello", he said. "Do you know how to get to this village....?"

He mispronounced it in his English accent but I was familiar with the many and varied pronunciations of the village name by both English and overseas visitors. I corrected the name and told him the direction before riding on again. I noted that his cornflower blue sweater matched his eyes. Then I saw him again a few days later, when I was 'on earlies' and serving breakfast at the hotel. The hotel was full of plus fours gents and enough military bark to inhibit Her Majesty herself. The staff labelled the men 'old buffers of the salmon fishing variety' but more recently the guests also included a younger professional contingent newly appointed by some of the developing Welsh Valley Industries and paid for by their respective companies. The man I had briefly met in the woods was one of the latter. The Glaisfar County Hotel was at a fair distance from the Welsh Valleys which pleased its workforce. It was commutable by car and the hotel offered the classy comfort of a shabby but comfortable country residence, which is what it used to be before Sir Rob's father bought it and converted it into a hotel. As usual with any place owned by Sir Rob, little money was spent on repair work and hotel maintenance. When I worked there, its fading grandeur still held some commercial credence, but even then the bedrooms in winter were reputed to be damp and American guests complained of mildew on their shoes if they left them overnight in the wardrobe. The large double bedrooms were almost unheatable with their high ceilings beneath a leaking roof and weather-challenged guttering. But the hotel grounds were beautiful and lovingly tended by an old Fenton retainer called 'Glyn the Gatehouse' because he lived in a small house with a circular roof at the entrance to the main gate. Glyn was always cheerful and very attached to the word 'lovely'.

"Hello, lovely day for catching a couple of lovely pheasant. Yes, it's a lovely run down to the river and you know mun, lovely trout around at this time of year".

The three of us were greatly amused by Glyn and would imitate his accent:

"It's a shame about that lovely boy who drowned in the lovely river. He had a lovely death in the whirlpool mind you, and a lovely funeral, mun".

On one occasion, Mrs Klein overheard our impersonations of Glyn and our flippancy annoyed her. She sharply dismissed Pearl and me to our homes with admonishments on our 'dark' humour. We were upset and embarrassed, unable to understand why Juliet Klein took life so seriously. Dora and my mother would never be provoked by anything as trivial as that. My mother would more likely want me to continue with the imitation of Glyn to even more absurd heights whilst Dora would find the perfect excuse to focus on Pearl's idle hands that could be applied more effectively to café work rather than to satirical commentary. On occasions such as these, neither of us envied Anna Klein.

"I found the village", said the man with a slightly tanned complexion and cornflower blue eyes. He looked up at me smiling, allowing space for me to place his plate of bacon, scrambled eggs, tomatoes, mushrooms and sausages.

"You gave very good directions".

"Well, I do live there" , I said rather awkwardly, hoping the toast went on the right as Iris the head waitress had told me.

"Outside in Sian, for cutlery outside in. Move further left or you'll pour the drink over the guests".

The handsome man continued gently:

"I'd like you to show me a little of this area. I may be moving here someday. If you have some time that is."

I was really flattered by his attention but I really couldn't understand why he wanted me to show him the area. I showed off by telling my grandmother who reacted sharply saying that the guest was 'a dirty old man' and under no circumstances was I to go out alone with him. "Sian, I'll speak to Iris. She agreed to look after you. I can't have the worry of this. Your mother takes no responsibility as usual and we cannot have a repeat of her mistakes".

I immediately rushed to mollify her saying I would never go with him alone and that he was leaving the hotel at the end of the week anyway. My grandmother looked relieved but I felt bad about deceiving her. Nevertheless, I desperately wanted to go out with Harold Stanton because I was very drawn to him and the sophistication of his world so different to the narrowness and deep-rooted despondency of my own. I dreamt about him and could not get his face out of my mind. I had never had a crush on anyone like I had on Harold Stanton.

I showed Harold (everyone called him 'Hal') around the area one Saturday when my family believed I was working at the hotel. In the afternoon we drove to a pub near Ross on Wye and had lunch. It was a warm sunny day and we strolled along the river path at Symonds Yat, admiring the view of three counties, each providing a glimpse of their rich expanse beyond the river and beyond the outline of the woods and hills. Hal walked with his arm loosely draped around my shoulders. I felt warm and protected as well as ecstatic. I was wildly attracted to him, experiencing overwhelming feelings of longing that no boyfriend - even the long lost Wyn - had even come close to triggering. I put Hal on a pedestal because he was handsome, educated, cultured with admirable social ease. He was twenty-seven, a civil engineer from Amersham in Buckinghamshire and one of the newly appointed professionals to Welsh Valley Industries. He was currently working on a temporary contract for some months so I was devastated to learn that he would eventually leave South Wales. I told myself not to think about it. But then there was an even greater problem: Hal was married. He did not hide the fact that he had been married three years and he had a two-year-old daughter. I took in this information unflinchingly before I went to bed with him. But at the time I told myself it did not matter because all I wanted was to be with him and the rest was irrelevant. Perhaps I had inherited more of my mother's genes than I cared to acknowledge but part of me sensed, even at the best times during our short and fleeting relationship, that it was bound to end badly.

Hal kissed me that same afternoon we walked along the River Wye. When I responded, he asked me if I was prepared to have sex with him. I said I didn't know - I wasn't sure. He kissed me again and then drove up a steep hill overlooking Symonds Yat to the Forest of Dean, a very isolated spot popular with birdwatchers, keen on catching a glimpse of the rare kestrel In the forest. Hal removed my underwear and began to caress my body in a way that I had never known before. The teenage fumblings of immature boys was nothing compared to this. It was sexual awakening but it also brought anxiety, guilt and shame because I knew what I was doing was wrong and that my grandmother would have been horrified.

"Darling, are you still a virgin?"

"Yes", I answered shyly.

"Then we'd better do this at the hotel. It's going to be difficult here - in the open air".

Sex hurt and at first I did not enjoy it. Hal was an encouraging and experienced lover but I continued to be shy and very frightened of getting pregnant. When I anxiously raised the subject; he looked worried - saying he would use a condom next time. But he only ever used it once and not successfully, as I remember. I told Hal that 'nice girls don't have intercourse until they marry, especially with dirty old men' - at least that is what my grandmother believed. We were lying naked after sex on his large double bed on the second floor of the hotel, with the blood orange sun sinking slowly into the shadows behind the Table Mountain. Hal tickled my nose with a piece of dried pampas grass from a small blue vase that adorned all guests' room service trays.

"And do you agree with your grandmother?"

"Yes," I said seriously. "But you are not so old. Anyway, my grandmother would die if she realised I was here with you".

He frowned.

"Better not tell her then".

We could not be seen together locally as it would cause gossip with serious repercussions for us both. It was the period of the Profumo scandal that involved powerful politicians and young call girls. I remember how horrified my grandmother was by the sexual precocity of eighteen-year-old Mandy Rice-Davies.

"Sian is like a child compared to that Mandy Rice. The cheap bit looks twice Sian's age. I blame those dirty old men".

I squirmed on the long oak settle in the kitchen, feeling guilty. What if she found out about Hal and me? I knew I should end the affair but I couldn't bear the thought of life without Hal but there wasn't much hope of a life with him either. I told my grandmother nothing because I knew it would hurt her so much. But she just didn't understand how I felt. I wanted to experience the excitement of being in love, of having illicit sex, of going beyond the drab existence I had experienced up until now. I wanted more; I wanted so much more. In spite of what my grandmother said, I really envied the freedom of Mandy Rice-Davies.

Hal encouraged me to go out and enjoy myself with friends of my own age but I resented his suggestions, suspicious of an ulterior motive - like getting rid of me. In reality, I had few friends and my closest acquaintances failed miserably to compensate for the loss of Anna and Pearl. The Beatles music was all the rage and many of my contemporaries loved rock concerts, but I attended very few because of logistics. Getting back to the village from Foistneth was impossible without personal transport as the last bus left at eight o'clock before dances and rock concerts had barely started. Consequently, my social life was almost entirely dependent on Hal. Perhaps I missed him more because there were so very few distractions; I really don't know. All I do know is that I couldn't wait to see him again at the breakfast table on Monday mornings after he returned home from spending the weekend with his family in Buckinghamshire. But we had to be hyper-vigilant at the hotel because should Iris cotton on, she would not hesitate to alert my grandmother. I knew Hal would lose his professional standing in the community should our sexual exploits become public. This was not London or LA but a rural backwater in South Wales where a married Englishman having an affair with a seventeen-year-old local girl, ten years his junior, would not be looked upon with tolerance for human frailty and I would be branded as 'cheap' and without morals. I dreaded to think what example would be made of us by the Reverend Morgan-Morgan in his Sunday morning sermon on the wickedness of Jezebel.

Hal hired rooms in hotels on the border with England and at other times, we made love in his roomy Bentley car. Outside of the bedroom, we had very little in common. My social life was narrow and I was raw and inexperienced in most things. Because our family had no car, I knew few places outside of Wales and had only been to London once, on a school trip. I knew a lot about 'aspects of the novel' because I was studying English literature for A Level but Hal was not interested in classical novels or history - my other great academic love - and he had never even heard of Rousseau. He was very keen on football but I had no interest in it. Theodore was the only one in our family that went to watch the local matches. But we did share a love of cinema. We saw 'Spartacus' and it made me shed tears. Another time we saw a film called 'Butterfield 8' with Elizabeth Taylor about an illicit love affair between a businessman and a prostitute. The mood of the film was darkly brooding with an ominous message to those who break society's rules. It made me feel ashamed and unhappy. Sex was a serious issue and the social arguments for sexual liberation and the advent of feminism were the prerogative of the educated and privileged middle classes in London - and moviemakers of course.

Sometimes after the cinema we would have a meal in an Indian restaurant where Hal would enjoy a cigar with his brandy and I would have a small glass of red wine. I had never been to a proper restaurant before I met him and he was amused by my obsession with the positioning of the cutlery and crockery. We had ways of giving each other the odd look or glance across the table of the hotel when I was serving him. Even when I didn't serve his table, I was very aware of his presence. I dreaded the day when the summer holidays would end and I would return to Foistneth Grammar School. Hal asked me what I intended to do with my life after school and I said I didn't really know. I just wanted to leave home.

Then unexpectedly one morning, the most dreaded scenario of all happened. Hal arrived at the hotel breakfast table with his wife and daughter. There had been no advance warning, no time to prepare me for the event. He told me later that his wife had insisted on visiting that particular weekend and would not accept no for an answer. I wondered whether she was suspicious that he was seeing another woman and had come along to check for herself. He said this was not the case at all but he had promised her a week at the Glaisfar in the early days before our affair and she was now holding him to it. Hal's wife had been a PA to his former manager. She was also a relative of the managing director of the company he worked for in Amersham. He told me that they had fallen in love with Julia almost immediately and married before either of them really had time to reflect on what they were doing. He said he regretted their rush into married life but not the marriage itself. I found all of this very baffling indeed and incomprehensible to my simplistic way of thinking. If he loved her why did he need to reflect on anything and if he didn't regret the marriage, what was he doing in bed with me? I was perfectly capable of writing one and a half thousand words on the complexity of Othello's relationship with Desdemona but totally incapable of comprehending the motives of the man I loved most in the world.

Chapter 7

Music: *'I can't stop loving you'*. Ray Charles (1962)

Julia Stanton was young, blonde and very pretty. I had dark hair, almost as dark as my mother's and I clung to the belief - possibly reinforced by Hollywood - that 'gentlemen prefer blondes'. Pearl was living evidence of it as she had always had better-looking suitors than Anna and myself, until now that was. Their charming little daughter Elizabeth was also blonde and she resembled her father. I kept my eyes demurely on the tablecloth when I served them at breakfast and did not look at Hal. I felt rather than saw his ill ease. Once, when I was at the back of the dining-room I glanced into the long, narrow mirror tightly pinned to the back wall where additional crockery and cutlery were laid out on a starched white tablecloth. I saw him lightly touch his wife's hand and I caught sight of an intimate glance between them that couples often share, comfortable in the knowledge of each other. I felt the green-eyed monster of jealousy tearing away at my heart. I was distraught and found it hard to concentrate on my work and was criticised for not loading the dishwasher properly. I ended up bursting into tears and sobbing in the corner of the kitchen. Iris came and comforted me but was surprised at my new-found sensitivity to tickings-off. I got along well with the staff and was now very self-assured with the waitressing work. Iris asked me if I was 'coming on' and sent me home after breakfast. I was glad to go as my eyes were red and swollen and I didn't want Hal to see me like that. The staff all talked about *her*.

"She's really nice isn't she, Mrs Stanton? A pretty woman too. Mind you, he's good looking himself. They must miss each other though. You can tell how much he loves her."

I prayed she would leave before the week was out but she did not. He frequently took her out and walked around the grounds with her, his arm draped across her shoulders. I hated him for that and wondered whether he had taken her out to places like Symonds Yat and the Forest of Dean where we had had some splendid walks and shared intimate moments. On the following weekend, the Stanton family returned to Buckinghamshire and he returned alone very early on the Monday morning. My purgatory was over but I realised I needed a few things clarified within our relationship.

Dear Pearl,

Everything is well again and Hal and I are as much in love as ever.

"What a load of baloney", I thought as I crossed out the sentence from the letter I had just started. Yes, I loved Hal but he had never said he loved me. It was two weeks since his wife's departure and autumn was beginning to set in. In ten days' time my job at the hotel would finish and I would return to school. What then? What would happen then? I was writing my letter at the clumsy home-painted dressing table I had turned into a desk for studying. I glanced out of my bedroom window and felt an overwhelming stifling sadness. My mother was still at the hospital for most of the week and it was agreed that she had a temporary bed in the dining-room until she moved back into the house permanently. I needed more space for my A Level books and also privacy to study. I had to admit that our present arrangements suited me better even though there were times when I missed my mother. My grandmother had become more withdrawn and seemed distracted by her own thoughts. Theo spent a lot of time at Mattie's and rarely came home to sleep anymore. The house felt lonely and empty. It was also shabby and smelled of damp and my grandmother ruminated about no longer having the energy to decorate ceilings and walls. I had offered to help her but that summer I was too busy with Hal to give Davy Cottage much thought. I glanced across the lovingly tended lawn with its rapidly fading flower beds and caught sight of my grandmother bending down in her green pinafore as she pulled out some weeds and dead plants from the borders circling the grass. As she looked up, I waved to her. I felt despondent and fearful. I knew I was pregnant; I had all the obvious symptoms. I had missed two periods and my breasts had started to swell and feel tender. I could not break the news to my grandmother as she would have been so angry and disappointed. She was very proud of my academic achievements and would inform close acquaintances that 'Sian is taking her A Levels this year and we hope she will continue to University in due course.'

I snatched a fresh sheet of my lined writing-pad and wrote desperately:

> *Anna, please ask your father if he knows someone who can help me. I'm pregnant and I don't know what to do.*

I told Hal about my suspected pregnancy some days after the return of his wife to Buckinghamshire. He looked worried and asked me if I had told anyone. I lied and said no but in effect I had given Anna permission to speak to her father in confidence as I knew the doctor could be discreet; he had proved himself to be on so many other occasions. Hal 'assumed' I would have an abortion and said he would enquire about where I could receive help. I was due back at school the following week and was already beginning to experience nausea in the mornings. Nightmares about knitting needles and back-street abortions would crowd into my dreams causing me to awake abruptly in the night. Despair flooded into my very being and I sweated with fear. I had read about illegal abortions in novels and they made me feel sick with apprehension as I tried to block the images from my mind. But fear of my grandmother knowing was greater than my fear of a knitting needle. There was no one in my family to turn to. My father's sister lived in Plymouth but I did not know where. His mother had died many years before and I had had little to no contact with her. The Bayley family had originally settled in Ebbw Vale but both my father and his older sister Laura were born and lived in the South of Ireland as young children because their mother was Irish. My paternal grandfather was known as 'Puffer Bayley' because (they said) he even slept with a pipe attached to his lips. My paternal grandparents moved to Ebbw Vale in the 1930s in search of a living although Puffer was originally from Ebbw Vale. The South Wales Valleys had a steady flow of work to offer in the coal mines and feeder industries in the 1930s which was the reason for my grandparents' uprooting from Ireland and settling in South Wales. Puffer was a violent father and a drunk but Laura escaped the chaotic family home by marrying a manager from a local tool factory where she worked during the war. She and her husband moved to Plymouth taking her mother with them. Left on his own with his pipe and his son Cliff who refused to leave with his sister, Puffer eventually found a crumbling cottage in our village in a dire state of disrepair and he moved in there with his son. My parents met at one of the local Whist Drives or local dances, I can't remember which. My father was doing all sorts of odd jobs at the time from digging up the roads in order to lay new water pipes, working with the timber merchant of ill repute, Capt. Ferris-Brown, whose tomb we had frequently played on as children beneath the span of the grim angel's wings that attempted to hide Dora and the deacon from our innocent curiosity. Sadly, Cliff became homeless when, in a drunken stupor, his father dropped his lighted pipe onto the bed and it set the eiderdown alight. That was the end of Puffer, the eiderdown and even the cottage but Cliff was working late that evening at 'The Spinning Knight' and escaped a very painful and tragic fate. But it did not stop my grandmother acerbically stating: "gambling in the back rooms of the Spinning Knight more like". Ironically his addiction to gambling saved him from the carnage that was to follow. My father then ended up lodging with my grandmother for a while and his relationship with my mother further developed from there. When my mother became pregnant with me, her parents finally gave their permission for her to marry Cliff Bayley. She was married in a Registry Office in Foistneth and only her father attended the wedding. These are the bare bones of my parents' brief romance as disclosed to me. I never dared to ask for more detail because although my family guffawed unanimously at the Puffer story, they were too awkward and emotionally repressed to talk openly about how they really felt or the difficulties experienced in their own past lives.

Anna finally responded in a letter saying her father would examine me to ensure that I was pregnant before the next step was taken. Hal was informed and he seemed relieved that I had managed to take action without involving him directly. He drove me to Cardiff railway station where I was met by Anna and Dr Klein. My pleasure at seeing Anna was dimmed by the seriousness of the occasion and Dr Klein's unsmiling face. Hal did not stay with me to meet the Kleins but agreed a meeting later on in the afternoon, outside the station. On this particular weekend he stayed in South Wales, telling his wife he was working overtime on a project. Anna looked taller and thinner than I remembered her a year ago. She also looked very pale. She was wearing an unfashionable calf-length skirt and her best feature, her long, luxuriant dark hair, was hidden under a black beret-style hat. I remember hugging Anna on the station that early autumn day. The weather had changed and after almost a full eight weeks of warm weather it had now turned cold and overcast. Accustomed to the enveloping warmth of Hal's car, I had dressed far too thinly and sensed that Dr Klein did not approve of my mini dress, showing the greater part of my long, slim legs. It was not the reunion it should have been. Dr Klein drove us to his surgery in a residential part of Cardiff in total silence. He only said an odd word to Anna, sitting next to him. I felt like a leper, an outcast, a sinful woman who murders her own child. I was desperately unhappy, with churning thoughts of rejection by my friends and family and intense feelings of guilt. There was no Saturday surgery and in any case Dr Klein's partners were both observant Jews and did not work on the Sabbath. Dr Klein unlocked the surgery and let us in. He then proceeded to examine me and take a urine sample. It was not a pleasant experience. Anna told me that when she approached her father later, Dr Klein appeared both annoyed and concerned. In addition, he was not pleased with his daughter's involvement in the affair but he agreed to keep it a secret from his wife, knowing how the consequences would very likely affect Anna's friendship with me. Through a distant relative who was a GP in South London, he knew of a private clinic that carried out terminations and he had recommended it to other 'unfortunate girls' like myself. Dr Klein did not approve of abortion but he respected the right of the individual to make a choice. He also knew how hopeless my situation was. I was very young, unqualified for any job that would provide me with enough money to support myself and a child. My lover was married and unlikely to leave his wife. My grandmother's health was failing and the shock of my pregnancy could kill her, whilst my mother was a patient in a mental hospital and my uncle a tight-fisted egotist with little compassion or thought for others. The environment was hardly conducive to rearing an emotionally healthy child. I fantasised about the child but even at seventeen I was a realist, knowing I had been a reckless fool and that I was paying the price for it. My grandmother had warned me so many times:

"Sian will rush in where angels fear to tread. Think Sian, count ten. You are so impulsive."

Doctor Klein took us for lunch at an Italian restaurant and all of a sudden became more talkative. He quizzed me a lot about Hal and my family, especially my mother. He seemed surprised that she was still at the mental hospital for most of the week. He ran me back to Cardiff railway station at two thirty and Anna waited with me at the station until Hal arrived close to three. She would then take the bus home. Juliet Klein had gone to synagogue with her sons and Anna ostensibly was meant to be studying with a friend for an important school test on Monday. For his wife's information, Dr Klein was meant to be visiting a very sick patient and this good deed religiously exonerated him from Sabbath duties at the synagogue. The sun was struggling to come out as we drank our umpteenth cup of stale British Rail tea. Anna now drank tea without milk and said she did not eat any non-kosher food at home anymore. Since their move to Cardiff, her mother insisted on the family observing the Jewish dietary laws which excluded seafood and pork among other things. At this point, I reminded her of 'Wilf's caff' and Palethorpes' pork pies; we fell about laughing at Dora and Wilf's past antics, oblivious to our current problems and unpredictability of our futures. I was proud to introduce Hal to Anna but she said many years later that she couldn't understand what I saw in him.

"He's good looking but a bit of a smoothie".

Hal said Anna was plain and dressed like an Orthodox Jew. I didn't know what an 'Orthodox Jew' meant and I asked for clarification. His explanation of not switching on lights and cookers on Friday nights confused me more, particularly since I had vivid memories of one of Laurence's favourite pastimes which was switching the household lights on and off regardless of which day of the week it was.

I was pregnant. Dr Klein contacted the relative's clinic in London where I could have the abortion but I needed to get the money from 'my boyfriend'; it was expensive. Strange, but I never quite thought of Hal as a boyfriend. After the operation I would need to stay at the clinic overnight. Dr Klein also suggested I find somewhere to stay for a few days to recuperate as I needed someone with me should I start bleeding heavily; I must not lift anything heavy or engage in any strenuous activities. I squirmed with discomfort at the thought of bleeding to death and the heavy price I was paying for being reckless with both my body and my morals. The image of Pearl suddenly flashed into my mind; the Mellor-Clarkes had many times mentioned to Pearl to invite a friend to stay and here was a desperately sought opportunity. It would entail exorbitant costs to stay in London for a whole week and there was the additional problem of my remaining alone as no one was available to stay with me for that length of time. Dr Klein pointed out that Banbury was close enough to London so if there were any problems with the operation and I had to be re-admitted to the clinic, the distance was considerably shorter than from the district of Foistneth. The thought of this terrified me and I wished Anna had not been so explicit when repeating her father's medical precautions. She had agreed to meet me in London and accompany me to the clinic in Brixton. I cried into my pillow at home that night, realising that it was time I grew up and started taking responsibility for myself. I refused to think of the child that was about to be aborted as I could not allow myself to change my mind under any circumstances.

I experienced a tearful parting from Hal in early November when arrangements for my termination were finally completed. We agreed he would meet me in Foistneth after my return from Banbury. I was only going to be away nine days. He gave me the money in cash for the abortion and an extra thirty pounds for expenses. Dr Klein telephoned him at the Glaisfar and although I never learned the actual content of the conversation, Hal was very put out about it and said "Klein was abrupt, judgmental and domineering. Not qualities suited to a bedside manner in a doctor". But I found myself defending Dr Klein because not only was he the father of one of my dearest friends but because he had always been supportive towards me. Things would indeed be worse for all of us without Dr Klein's practical help and support, and Hal should be the first to recognise this. But Hal appeared disconcerted by my views and when he tenderly kissed me goodbye the day before a reluctant Theo ran me to Foistneth railway station, I sensed his feelings of relief.

I told my grandmother I was visiting Pearl in Oxfordshire and the only time convenient to the Mellor-Clarkes was November. I had to take a week off school but I was in the sixth form and we did not have daily lessons anymore. Anna and I met in the Wimpey bar at Paddington Station and more or less immediately went on our quest of the clinic in Brixton. We lost our way several times on the London Underground and ended up going Southeast when we should have been heading Southwest. We were both overly anxious about not getting to the clinic in time for my appointment, even though we had given ourselves two hours to get from Paddington to Brixton. In the end we had only 30 minutes to spare before my appointment with the doctor. I underwent a medical examination and it was agreed I would be admitted the following morning. The termination would take place in the afternoon. I handed over the money to a receptionist with painted eyes reminiscent of Nefertiti. She told me as she counted the cash that I would remain in the clinic overnight on Saturday. Dr Klein had arranged for Anna to stay with cousins of hers in Northwest London, ostensibly for Anna to visit a couple of medical schools before applying for the course the following year. One of Anna's distant cousins was a dentist trained at Guy's Hospital; he had agreed to show Anna around. It was the only explanation acceptable to her mother who would have been against the idea of Anna accompanying me to London, especially if she had been aware of the real reason for our visit.

I booked into my shabby bed and breakfast accommodation in Brixton as near as possible to the 'Well Woman Clinic' and Anna returned to her relatives in Northwest London. I sat looking at the dingy one-barred electric fire that devoured shilling coins like a voracious animal. The place was £8 a night and it was unbelievably shabby and basic. The single bed barely fitted into the room and was crammed up against the wall and accessible from one side only. Hanging unevenly above the gloomy fireplace was a faded picture of roses in a chipped frame. The net curtains were black from the accumulated dust and dirt of time. There was an unheated shared bathroom on the same landing, with brown stains clearly visible on the bath. I burst into tears after Anna had left, feeling sorry for myself and overwhelmed by an agonizing loneliness and feelings of despair. I thought enviously of Anna sitting around the welcoming table of her large Jewish family, having food pressed on her and congratulated on her career choice. She said she thought 'some nice Jewish boys' would be dragged along to meet her as the North London Jewish community was akin to one large marriage bureau. My outside show of bravado had totally crumbled as I slowly realised the seriousness of my situation.

I might die whilst having the termination and not one of my family even knew where I was. I would never see Hal again. Did he think about what was happening to me? Did he care? Even Anna had left me and gone home. Tears rushed to my eyes and flooded down my cheeks. Few times in my life had I felt so utterly alone and abandoned.

The meter clicked suddenly making me jump as the electric bar of the fire impulsively leaped from red back to its original dismal grey. The little heat there was disintegrated into nothing, leaving me shivering on the rickety bed. I had no choice but to seek refuge between the sheets in order to keep warm and eventually I fell into a restless sleep full of unnerving images. I kept seeing myself lying on an operating table with masked doctors pulling a baby out from between my legs whilst I kept screaming: "No stop, stop! I've changed my mind!" I also dreamed that Hal was there and his arms were around me and I felt so loved and secure.

"It's okay my darling", he kept saying "you'll be fine. You don't have to go through with this."

Tears of love and gratitude rushed warmly through my very being but the doctors did not stop and I cried out to Hal to stop them but unexpectedly he pulled away leaving me screaming silently. All sounds ceased abruptly apart from an insistent banging in the distance. Suddenly I became aware of a voice shouting:

"Sian Bayley, Sian Bayley, telephone" .

I struggled out of bed in a daze, whilst a gradual shocking realisation dawned on me; I was in a shabby hotel near the clinic where I would have an abortion tomorrow. I tightly clutched at my dressing-gown I wore to bed because the bed was freezing with its threadbare covers. Not even Davy Cottage at its worst in winter was as bad as this. I so longed for Hal to be on the phone, although the rational part of me insisted it would be highly unlikely as he did not know where I was. But I could not conceal my disappointment when I heard Anna's low voice:

"Sian, I thought I'd give you a quick ring. I've told my relatives I'm ringing home so I'll have to be quick. I can't come in the morning as my cousin Joe is insisting on taking me around some medical schools. There's not much point as they are closed but he insists on showing me their location. I have managed to get some free time tomorrow early evening so I'll come as soon as I can. It's really annoying but I can't wriggle loose of the family. How are you?"

"How do you expect when you've just woken me up to tell me you are not coming tomorrow. I wish to God Pearl had come instead of you. I could have counted on her."

"Sian, that's unfair. I'm doing my best. You have no idea how intrusive Jewish families can be. The only reason I can shake Joe off tomorrow afternoon is that I've told the family I'm visiting a very nice 'shiksa' (non-Jewish girl) friend so Joe's mother is not keen on Joe tagging along to meet you. I've had to invent all sorts of lies about your family in London."

"I'm sorry, Anna. I'm sorry. I feel so alone and terrified about tomorrow. I don't mean to sound off... but it's horrible here."

"It'll be okay Sian, you'll see. It's only one night in that shithole, thank God! You know where the clinic is. Wanting to, you can walk there. I promise I'll be there in the afternoon, around four at the latest. You may have had your operation by then but if not, I'll be there with you".

I went back to bed feeling exhausted and muddled but the phone call had helped somehow, allowing me to feel less alone. Eventually I dozed off but this time myriad images fought for transcendence in my subconscious, including the abstract figure of Joe's mother and her acute horror of 'a shiksa' in her son's life.

Anna actually arrived at the clinic before 3 p.m. the following afternoon. She brought some black grapes and spent about thirty minutes reassuring me before my operation as I felt very frightened of the operation but she had to leave before I came around from the anaesthetic. I was in a semi-comatose state from the various pain killers administered but not in any physical pain. I experienced pangs of guilt and remorse about the termination itself and as I sobbed aloud, I heard a nurse whisper:

"We'd better move her or she will upset the others."

I will never forget those mumbled words or the emotional blend of hopelessness and relief that I felt that night. The following morning, I learned President Kennedy had been assassinated. I would never forget where I was when JFK died. I pondered on this as I went to

Paddington Station alone to catch the train to Oxford. Thinking of the Kennedys kept my mind off my own misery and profound unhappiness. Anna telephoned me that evening at Pearl's. I was in good humour as Pearl and I were just consuming our second bottle of red wine and discussing the Kennedy assassination. I handed over the hall telephone to Pearl as Anna wanted to have a brief word and returned to Pearl's spacious bed-sitting room on the first floor of the farmhouse, where we both had been sprawled earlier on, drinking and smoking. When Pearl came back she declared solemnly:

"Anna said to look after you."

She gave me a big hug. I started to cry with the pleasure of knowing that both Pearl and Anna loved me very much and that I was indeed fortunate to have such devoted and caring friends. I swore then that I would always be there for them should they need me at any time in their lives. In the future I would be called upon to keep my promise but I can honestly say that I never broke the pledge I took that day.

Pearl had the following weekend off but she had to look after the Mellor-Clarke children and carry out her usual chores during the week. I spent time in my room resting as I was told by the clinic to rest for at least seven days after the operation. Grace Mellor-Clarke expressed some concern about the time I was spending alone in my room and suggested I went walking or riding in the countryside. She said it was unhealthy for a young girl to spend so much time resting. But we invented a plausible story about my being thrown from a horse in Foistneth called 'Black Bess' and how the awkwardness of the fall had caused some bruising to my spine, making walking painful and resting essential. I thought with some irony of how Black Bess was incapable of throwing anyone. Her drunken owner, Bob Roberts, would fall out of the Spinning Knight on a Saturday evening calling raucously:

"Bessie girl, where are you Bessie girl?"

He would then attempt a whistle whilst rocking backwards and forwards on his unsteady gaitered legs. Black Bess had more sense than her master. She would slowly waddle from where she had been loosely tethered in the carpark of The Spinning Knight, neighing loudly as she moved. She would stop by Bob who would attempt to mount her but fail miserably the first couple of times. An occasional passer-by would stop and try to push Bob upwards and towards the saddle but Bob was unable to co-ordinate his leg movements and swing his left leg over the side of the horse whilst keeping his right leg in the stirrup. Or he swung his leg too quickly and slithered off Black Bess on the opposite side. Locals had long given up helping Bob to mount and would tend to crowd inside the bay windows of the pub shouting:

"Come on Bessie girl, that's it. Up you go boy, up boy up! Goddamn it mun, move your bloody leg. Drunk as a skunk again. Connie'll 'ave you when you get 'ome!"

Finally, Bob would sit astride the horse and click the stirrups to the sound of cheers and placed bets. Black Bess would then begin her sedate walk back to Bob's farm about a mile and a half away. When out of vision of the pub, he would slump over Bess in an alcohol induced stupor, oblivious to the direction of the horse's movements. But Bess plodded on towards the farmhouse door where she waited, neighing patiently until Bob's belligerent wife Connie appeared. Connie presented red-faced and menacing with a rolling-pin in her hand. Bob would then miraculously sober up and slide off Bess mumbling something about: "meeting a man in the pub who wanted a dog". Connie would tell him to "bloody get in". She would then take Bess to her stable and give her hay whilst Bob sneaked into the house quaking with fear of the rolling-pin and what would happen later. At least that was how the village tale went. Children were often threatened with Connie when they misbehaved:

"Look Connie's coming and she's got a rolling-pin!", well-meaning parents would tell their misbehaving three-year-olds.

Thinking back to these village events we laughed, feeling the warm pleasure of our shared childhood experiences. We remembered hanging over the gate to Black Bess' field, calling to the friendly animal who would trot up to us and allow us to pat her and rub her nose. Rarely did we enter the field as Bob had placed a large notice on the gate, ordering in a Sir Rob fashion: 'Keep Out. The Horse Kicks and Bites. Trespassers Will Be Prosecuted'.

We sometimes took sugar for Bess and rode her saddle-less around the field pretending to be circus performers. For various reasons ranging from money (myself) over-protectiveness (Anna) and free time (Pearl) none of us ever learned to horse ride as children in spite of the many opportunities for learning in the village.

On the sixth day of my stay Pearl took me into Oxford as she was given a weekend free of duties. Oxford overwhelmed me by its stately grandeur and sense of history. I walked with Pearl through the public courtyards of the University Colleges impressed by the long-haired students in their swirling black gowns. They looked knowledgeable and purposeful. Some of the dons wore mortarboards and their lofty manner and gait very much reminded me of the characters in the film 'Top of the Form' that I'd seen recently. A fellow with a walrus moustache tore by, reminiscent of the actor Jimmy Edwards who spent most of his film career playing silly headmasters in toffee-nosed private schools. Was art imitating life or the other way around? I thought of Hal a lot. He had gone to London University. I wondered whether he had looked anything like the self-confident and intent young men when he was their age. I loved Hal so much but I knew our affair would not last and although I desperately hoped to see him again, I knew, deep down, it was unlikely. Anna had told me clearly that her father had said my relationship with Hal had to end. I was furious with Dr Klein for daring to interfere in my personal life but knowing him as I did, I feared he might inform my grandmother if I failed to comply. Also, Pearl continued to say that Hal was too old for me and that he would never leave his wife and marry me. I said I was too young for marriage but I desperately wanted Hal to ask me. Each time the phone rang, I fantasised it was Hal and felt a knot in my stomach until it became clear that it was definitely not him on the line. To be logical, he did not even know where I was and I had not seen him since the Thursday before I left for London. He said then to contact him at the Glaisfar during the week if I needed to speak to him urgently, but I would have to be careful and disguise my voice or someone might recognise me. He suggested one of my friends telephone the Glaisfar on my behalf. It felt like months since I had seen him and I missed him so much. Pearl told me clearly not to be a fool as Hal had conveniently handed over his responsibility to Dr Klein.

"But he paid for the abortion", I kept saying.

"Well, so he should, he's earning enough money and he's also responsible for getting you pregnant. He should have been with you Sian at the clinic, can't you see that?" I hotly defended Hal's actions with tears of sadness in my eyes but I knew Anna and Pearl were right. As I heard my own lame excuses I was sharply reminded of my mother and her total denial of reality in all things where my father was concerned. Although I could not bring myself to telephone Hal, I decided to contact him on my return. I told myself I needed to see him just once more.

Oxford was buzzing with shops and restaurants. It was sunny day, unusually mild for November and there were beautifully decorated Christmas trees in the town squares and in the shops. Following Mrs Mellor-Clarke's directions we eventually found the Italian bistro with a reputation for trendy wholesome Italian dishes served with relatively cheap red wine. It was located in a basement cellar. We were shown to small table. Each table had in the centre of it an unusual, tilted bottle housing a candle that dripped green and red wax patterns from wide neck to broad base. A juke box boomed out 'Do You Want To Know A Secret' by Billy J. Kramer. We ordered home-made pasta, sipped wine and gossiped about the Mellor-Clarke's parenting skills. We also discussed Pearl's future and her decision to leave the Mellor-Clarke's employment indefinitely in the following autumn of 1964. We would both then be eighteen and Pearl had agreed to stay until the youngest child went to kindergarten. She was doing well financially as the Mellor-Clarkes had increased her wages, given her an extra evening of free time and had promised her the use of one of their cars if she passed her driving test the following month. Personally, I didn't find Grace Mellor-Clarke the easiest person to talk to but she was pleasant enough. Pearl had lost most of her Welsh accent and this surprised me when I first saw her at the station in Banbury. At times she sounded a little like Mrs Mellor-Clarke complete with Oxfordshire burr. Pearl looked embarrassed and blushed a little when I told her this.

Pearl had visited her parents in Foistneth for a very brief weekend in May of the previous year. I had not spoken to her on that occasion as Davy Cottage did not have a telephone so it was difficult to make any contact. In addition, her visit was brief and mainly in aid of her cousin June's wedding. June was the daughter of Brenda the Boast and her somewhat lethargic husband Wally, known locally as 'Wally Top Shop' as they had once run an ironmongers' situated at the top of a steep hill overlooking the town. Pearl said she was speechless by the grandeur of her cousin's wedding.

"Believe you me Sian, Auntie Brenda was on top form. She said June's betrothed was in the Horse Guards and Princess Margaret took a fancy to him - 'tall in his bearskin 'at' - she said, but he preferred our June".

She started to giggle in the same old way she used to giggle as a child. "Considering how many tall men wearing bearskins are in and around Buckingham Palace, I can't imagine why Princess Margaret would specifically desire June's intended. According to Auntie Brenda, everything at the wedding was the best money could buy. You know, June's train was five yards long and held by six bridesmaids, two maids of honour and three page boys. The wedding cake was six tiers high! Never has such a wedding been seen before in Foistneth and never will be again".

We both oohed and ah ed, imitating Pearl's Uncle Wally and his cronies' accents:

"Has anyone got a saw for this cake, mun? A knife is no good on them solid gold pillars of icing see! Not for the likes of we".

"Use the sheep shears, Wal. Nip off now that top tier and we'll 'ave a bit of kaerk (cake) afore we gaw!"

June's new husband and his family were highly embarrassed by the outlandish behaviour of June's relatives. They snatched up their crocodile handbags and departed for the convivial borders of England as soon as the wedding breakfast was over. Brenda kept circling her guests, glass in hand, saying with histrionic gestures - very like those of her sister Dora - "Our June's husband is in the Coldstream Guards and he trained at Sandhurst. Oh... he wears a bearskin hat. Oh, he's educated luv and guess what? Princess Margaret thinks the world of him!" The more wine Brenda drank the more outrageous the boast and the more repetitive the phrases. Eventually she sunk down into a chair and started to attack her sister Dora.

"Our Mam was dying of cancer and you didn't lift a finger to help her. Not a finger!"

"Oh, how could you? I was running the cafe and I had two children, younger than yours. Oh, you are wicked you are, Bren", responded Dora also flushed by the liberal consumption of Harvey's Bristol Cream and numerous glasses of red wine. Pearl also mentioned that Tim Lewis, the chapel deacon, had been invited for some inexplicable reason and when Dora got drunk he escorted her outside where she was discovered by Wilf weeping into the deacon's arms about the state of her soul. Wilf was angry and refused to speak to his wife for weeks afterwards but Dora was indeed fortunate that she was discussing her soul and not anything else when her husband appeared on the scene. But I stopped short from asking Pearl whether she knew of her mother's affair with Tim Lewis.

Pearl said she left Foistneth this time under a family thundercloud and with many mixed emotions. Surprisingly, Dean had not been his usual obnoxious self and appeared a little intimidated by his sister's newly developed confidence and English accent. Pearl felt a little guilty about the brief visit but relieved she would not have to put up with Wilf's uncommunicativeness when angry; lethal silences that permeated throughout the household causing everyone to feel miserable and uneasy, even Dean. Wilf's 'silent treatment' was renowned for lasting for weeks on end, even months. When he finally came out of his mood, his family were unable to remember what the original cause of their offending behaviour had been but they were so eager and relieved to 'get back to normal' that they did not bother to ask for any clarification. Pearl commented on 'dad's moods' and how as a child she always thought that other dads gave their families 'the silent treatment' when annoyed. She commented that the Mellor-Clarkes had the odd row and they sometimes shouted at each other but it was not followed by a sadistic 'silent treatment'.

"You know Sian", said Pearl digging into her lasagne, "Foistneth looked so small and shabby - with the outstanding exception of Auntie Brenda's wedding party - and everything looked a bit shrunken somehow, different to how I remember it. How strange! Anyway, I'm going home for Christmas this year but I can't say I'm looking forward to it after what happened on that weekend. But I will see you next time I visit, won't I?"

It was late November but Christmas felt like a year away. Where else would I be anyway? I would spend a lonely and boring Christmas with my grandmother, mother and Theodore, as I had every other year of my life. Suddenly, I felt warm liquid surging down my legs and I doubled over in pain. I sprang to my feet in embarrassment and tore along the narrow passageway of the restaurant crowed with tables towards the toilet in the far corner praying the blood running down my legs would not be visible to other diners. I was lucky, the toilet was not far from our table and I breathed with relief as I locked the door and inspected the damage to my clothes. My trousers were slightly stained with blood but with my long cardigan over the top I would be able to disguise the flow. I had brought sanitary things with me to change as I was still bleeding heavily some days. I told Pearl we needed to leave the restaurant immediately as I felt messy, humiliated and angry about what had happened and how things had turned out. I didn't feel in control of anything anymore. I felt as confused as ever, blown along a tortuous path that seemed to have no specific direction. I wanted to be happy and I was envious of Pearl living a more stimulating and settled life at the Mellor-Clarkes. Ironically, most people in the village, except for my grandmother, had commented that Pearl was too young to leave home and if she was 'flighty like her mother' the chances were high that she'd be pregnant before she reached Oxfordshire. But I was the one who had got pregnant, practically on my own front doorstep.

Safely back at the farm, I took some pills and went to bed. I was relieved that next morning the heavy bleeding had stopped as I feared we may have had to do some explaining to the Mellor-Clarkes. I was glad to leave Oxfordshire the next day and to return to the familiar, if not safe, haven of my own home. Pearl drove me herself to the station in an old Land Rover. One of the farm workers with a driving licence sat next to her in the front whilst I sat in the back with my suitcase. We hugged our goodbyes on the station alone and promised each other to make contact at Christmas. Pearl also extracted from me a loose promise not to contact Hal but we both knew that I would. As the train pulled away, I leaned through the window and waved until Pearl's blonde head and her fashionable black and white 'op art' raincoat slowly faded from view. I then sat down and almost immediately felt the inner gloom descend again. I wished that I had never been born.

In less than a week I took a day off school unbeknown to my grandmother and cycled to the Glaisfar Hotel on the pretext of collecting my last wages. Memories of the place with its all too familiar blended smells of wax polish, Jayes disinfectant and fruit pudding with custard temporarily overwhelmed me. An outsize Christmas tree, sparkling with silver baubles and draped in tinsel occupied a prominent corner of the spacious reception area. Festoons of holly and mistletoe hung from the carved oak staircase and from other strategic positions where guests could view them at an advantage. I longed to go back in time to the early days of summer when I had first met Hal. I wanted to push back the hands of the clock and extinguish time. So much had happened in the last four months, particularly in the last ten days. I scoured the dining-room and bar for Hal but it was a Saturday and I knew he would not be there. Iris had spoken to the accounts clerk the day before about preparing my wages and she had my wage packet waiting. Iris was a nice woman, plain and friendly with no frills. She handed me the wage packet. "Well, I suppose you'll be too busy at school to come back here next year. But if you fancy the odd bit of work waiting table in the holidays or at weekends let me know."

I said I would but I knew that next year would be a very difficult one for me and I needed every spare hour to study for the exams ahead. I now totally accepted what my grandmother repeated many times: "the way out of the ghetto is via education" and "freedom applies only to the educated and of course, the rich". I took my A Level study very seriously as I had decided to leave Foistneth the following summer. I had no intention of ever returning on a permanent basis.

I made small talk with Iris asking about the regular guests, wildly hoping she would spontaneously mention Hal, but she did not. This left me with no choice but to challenge her openly. She looked at me sharply, causing me to blush.

"Mr Stanton's left Wales for good, Sian. It turned out that his wife was pregnant with their second and she insisted that he went home to Buckinghamshire. He moved out yesterday and from what I gather, he has no plans for returning here."

I made my goodbyes with superficial jollity but my mind felt dissociated from my body. I grasped the handlebars of my bike and pushed it past Glyn the Gatehouse who commented on 'a lovely day for a ride'. He also mentioned my 'lovely bike' and asked me to give his regards to 'your lovely grandmother'. I pushed the bike onto the path leading through Sir Rob's private wood. The river rushed alongside of me at the bottom of the steep bank with its medley of overhanging bushes. The naked trees were rapidly losing to winter any lingering autumnal hues and the green bushes along the riverbank bent fully forward, their fragile branches lightly caressing the river sides. But I saw none of it and felt a searing pain high up in my chest. I felt numb, unable to think, unable to feel. I reached the eight-arched stone bridge and I stopped suddenly when crossing it. I stood in one of the narrow niches of the bridge that allowed pedestrians to pull in and allow horses or motorcars to pass. I looked over at the River Usk. It was in full flow, similar to that barely remembered Christmas two years ago when Anna and I had almost drowned. Part of me wanted to end it all by throwing myself over the bridge and into the river. I wanted a dramatic oblivion that ended forever my unbearable emotional pain and I also wanted those who had injured me to weep with heart-torn guilt. But memories of the river episode were too vivid and I knew how physically uncomfortable and terrifying drowning would be. Silent breathless sobs engulfed me, frightening me into believing I was going mad. Finally, I calmed down and I hung intently over the bridge hoping a curious local would not go by whilst I was in such a state. I thought of how Hal had abandoned me without a thought. He had not rung; he had not written; he had left no message. It was patently clear to all except me, that Hal was only interested in saving his own position and reputation. He did not love me at all and I had been naive enough to believe that he was unhappy within his marriage and that our affair was important to him. Now I realised that I had been only a temporary distraction to him so he was able to discard me like a jaded object of little value when he perceived his lifestyle was threatened. Standing there on the bridge overlooking the relentless river in flood and with an overwhelming desire to end my own life, I came to understand that Harold Stanton only really loved one person and that person was Harold Stanton. I glanced along the main road with its sharp decline leading to the bridge. No one was in sight and the only sounds were the relentless swishing of the river and the persistent cries of distant birds. I stood still and focussed on the scene, the sounds, the smells, the hues of the majestic hills and my overwhelming physical and mental anguish. My grandfather's face with an expression of great sadness suddenly came to mind and the image stuck for some seconds. I made a decision; I got on my bike, took a deep breath, squared my shoulders and rode determinedly across the eight-arched bridge in the direction of Davy Cottage.

Chapter 8

Music: 'Time is on my side'. The Rolling Stones (1964)

The last year in the village was very different to the other years of my childhood. I had no friends and no boyfriend to distract me. I would occasionally stay behind at school and play tennis with some of my classmates and take a later bus home. On my last term at the Foistneth Grammar School, I worked hard academically as I desperately wanted to pass my exams and go to university. The thought of a dreary life in the surrounds of Foistneth spurred me on and was the main reason for my dedication to my books. Also, the old academic competitiveness between the three of us reared its determined head once again. Anna would progress to medical school and Pearl had already left Foistneth with a career in mind. I did not want to be the one left behind, envious of my friends and pitied by them. Then last but not least, there was my grandmother to whom I owed so much. I knew that going to university would give her so much pleasure. Therefore, I worked hard and stayed focussed on the ever advancing A Level examinations. School was easier in the sixth form where rules on school uniform were flexible and the teachers less forbidding and patronising. I was taking English Literature and French A Levels, mainly because I liked both the female teachers and learned well with them.

I managed to meet up with Pearl over the Christmas period and spent a few days with her at the caff. But things had changed; we had changed. We did not laugh at the same old things anymore and I worried whether we were growing apart. Pearl irritated me with her constant references to the Mellor-Clarkes and their comings and goings. Dean had quietened down because Wilf was keeping a very wary eye on him and there was no Pearl to blame for his bad behaviour. Dean had become accustomed to his sister not being around and had developed some friendships himself. He had no desire to tag along with us. Pearl said her parents, the caff and Foistneth made her feel sad and guilty because it was all depressing and she hated being there. Although more tolerant of Wilf, it was apparent that

Pearl had little empathy with Dora and she was often scathing in her comments to her mother. 'Elping in the shop' was no longer an option as Pearl refused to do it unless she spontaneously chose to. Pearl would sit and read ignoring her mother's comments like: "you should honour your father and mother, Pearl. I don't know what's got into you. We've done our best. Oh, kids today. Isn't it awful they are so ungrateful? The more you do the less they respect you." She would moan about this to her local customers without exception when Pearl was around. One day Pearl, tired of her mother's perpetual whining and criticising, stuck her head through the beaded curtain saying loudly "perhaps our defects were caused by the stinkerbum butter you raised us on". Dora, Wilf and Dean all gasped and Williams Backstreet who had just started visiting the caff again after years of voluntary exclusion burst into guffaws: "Good on you girl, that's the spirit! I remember that revolting stinkerbum myself and the cat sitting on them sherbet lemons!". As soon as the laughing Williams had left, Wilf came into the living quarters and walked up to his daughter. His face was deadly pale and we both froze as he woodenly approached us with his gangling gait. I cringed, fearing he would strike Pearl. "Putt..." he said, "get out of my house, you nasty piece of work. Don't ever speak to your parents like that again, in front of strangers. Putt....get out, NOW!".

"Very well", stammered Pearl but I could see she was quaking with fear. I need to get my things first.

"No", said Wilf, "get out now!"

"Wilf" said Dora, "Our Pearl will apologise..."

"No, I won't", said Pearl, tears now running down her face. "I despise you all and having to leave this dump is a pleasure. Let's go Sian!"

We snatched our coats and scarves and scurried out of the caff into the freezing December evening. We headed in the direction of the local bus station to catch a bus to the village where I lived. I fumbled in my pocket and found some spare change to telephone my grandmother. Theo had recently capitulated and a phone was now installed at Davy Cottage but he had stipulated that he would pay only for his *own* telephone calls. My grandmother agreed for Pearl to stay but Pearl had no clothes or makeup with her. Her face was stained with tears and I put my arm around her. This was not the glamorous woman in the

Mary Quant Op Art mackintosh that 'lunched in Oxford' but a frightened, mixed-up child who was being punished for the one time in her life when she plucked up enough courage to challenge her eccentric and insensitive parents.

We didn't know how long we would have to wait for a bus but finally the Wales Fargo bus crept alongside other parked buses and we boarded it shivering, our scarves pulled tight around our necks. We waited with chattering teeth and frozen feet inside the stone bus station; the floor stunk of urine, ineffectively camouflaged by a powerful disinfectant. Suddenly Dean appeared as if from nowhere carrying my suitcase into which Dora had stuffed a washbag, some makeup and night things belonging to Pearl. She had guessed where we were going. Dean reached us panting and gesticulating. He decided to hang around and wait with us for the departure of the bus, commenting on his father's irrational behaviour; for once he was in total admiration of his sister.

There were a few young soldiers from the local barracks sitting at the back of the bus and they whistled at us. We ignored them and sat near the front noting the occasional familiar village face boarding the bus. We pretended we did not recognise the faces so as not to get involved in small talk. Then Mattie Boyce got on the bus from a stop along the way. She looked very attractive in a short black and white checked coat and a white fur hat.

"Hello girls; how are you both? "

"Very well thank you, Mrs Boyce."

Polite protocols of the time forbade younger members of the population from using a married person's first name unless specifically told to do so.

"Call me Mattie, everybody does. Are you going home Sian? Give my regards to your grandmother".

I was amused by this as my grandmother was hostile to Mattie because of her involvement with Theodore. I never quite understood whether she saw Mattie as a financial threat to Davy Cottage or was merely annoyed by her son's involvement with a divorced woman of questionable morality whom he might be foolish enough to marry.

"Your Uncle T's staying with me tonight so Pearl can have his dinner", Mattie winked, knowing the full extent of my grandmother's opinion of her. Only Mattie could have called Theodore 'T' and we spent the rest of the journey giggling and commenting on this, our original upset forgotten. This was the Pearl I knew and loved, not 'Mrs Mellor-Clarke the Younger'.

Pearl stayed two nights with us and on the third day she returned home to collect her things and say goodbye to her family. Wilf wouldn't speak to her and dished out 'the silent treatment' to the whole family. Dora and Dean accompanied Pearl to Foistneth station the following morning and waved her goodbye. Pearl rang me herself that same evening when she arrived back in Banbury. She was very angry and upset with her father and pleased to be back at the farm. She swore vehemently to me that she would not return home again - unless one of her parents were ill - as her Christmas visit had been an unmitigated disaster that she did not ever care to repeat. She mentioned that she had made contact with Anna but that Anna had sounded 'a little strange on the phone'. I had only spoken to Anna once since my termination mainly because I had been busy with my schoolwork and day to day things. When I did call, Juliet Klein answered the telephone and was very abrupt. I believed she did not want me to be friendly with Anna because she did not think me 'good enough' for her daughter. I sensed her reluctance to call Anna to the phone so I never summoned up the courage to telephone Anna again.

Sir Rob had finally agreed to put a flushing lavatory and basic bathroom into Davy Cottage. We were fortunate that unlike so many of Sir Rob's properties we had cold running water in the kitchen whilst others in old properties had to rely on a water pump in the road that served the community. The earlier lavatory at Davy Cottage was a wooden privy in the garden. A bathroom had not been built because there was not enough space for it and in the early 20th century it was considered a luxury not a necessity as in the 1960s when government grants were offered to landlords to upgrade their property. Living conditions at Davy Cottage had been very harsh in those days when we had to cross the garden in freezing temperatures at night when we wanted to relieve ourselves. The alternative was to use the chamber pot under our beds and empty it in the morning. Stomach upsets caused a great deal of physical discomfort and acute embarrassment, particularly when sharing a bedroom with another person. Sir Rob had finally agreed to carry out a small downstairs extension to the property with added sanitary facilities although he increased the rent threefold making it difficult for my grandmother to meet his demands. When my mother returned from the hospital on a permanent basis, she was given a disability allowance which contributed considerably to the family expenses. Theo was paying much less since he was a permanent resident at Mattie's. It transpired that my mother was able to claim maximum social security benefit as my grandmother had no assets, only a small state pension.

These days has improved as I had now moved into Theo's room. He never slept there but he managed to keep some of his clothes in the wardrobe and occupied two of the four drawers of the dressing-table. He refused point-blank to remove his belongings saying in his flat monotone, "So long as I am paying the electricity bill, so long as I am paying anything here, my clothes stay in the dressing-table drawer." My grandmother slowly rid my room of them by bagging them up for jumble sales and the dustman. Theodore was unaware of their disappearance. Other times she would prepare some of his things in a neatly packed bag. When he dropped in on some business or other, she would tactfully suggest he took his belongings with him because the weather was getting 'colder', or 'warmer', or 'rainier'. He looked suspicious, but bit by bit, his presence disappeared from my bedroom and it slowly began to acquire my own personal stamp on it. I had space for my books and could leave them around open at a particular page when the need arose without fear of complaint from anyone. I put up posters of actors and rock stars and some photographs of my family. I had a photograph of my grandfather looking smart in a dark suit with a serious 'in pose' expression. It was old style, sepia photography in a damaged photo frame. There was another greatly faded black and white photograph of my grandmother as a younger woman with my mother standing at her knee and Theodore on her lap. Theodore had the same tightly coiled mousy hair and pursed lips as a baby as he had now. His grey eyes showed little enthusiasm for life but I did note that Baby Theodore bore a resemblance to my grandmother. My mother, on the other hand, was a female carbon copy of my grandfather. She looked a sad little girl in her lace-up leather boots and trailing white linen dress. My hair was a shade or two lighter than my mother's and according to her I resembled my father's side of the family, with the exception of my hair colour. In pride of place, on the narrow mantelpiece of the small bedroom fireplace, proudly stood the metal-framed photograph of the three of us together. It had been taken by Dr Klein when we were about fifteen and showed us standing with our arms around each other. We were pictured on a sunny summer's day, on the eight-arched bridge spanning the River Usk. Anna, positioned in the middle, looked ill at ease and gangly in a shapeless shift dress that did nothing to enhance her figure. I thought I appeared too plump but Pearl looked really pretty with her hair in a ponytail. I would often stare at this photo of us on the bridge whilst I was studying. From the bridge, the steep village road headed east in the direction of the Glaisfar Hotel and towards some very painful memories I wanted to forget but that I was too often tempted to recall.

During my last year at school, I did occasional kitchen and bar work at The Spinning Knight pub. It was literally a four-minute walk from Davy Cottage. I needed money to buy makeup and some fashionable clothes as money at home was always in short supply. I worked in the kitchen at weekends and after my eighteenth birthday I occasionally worked in the bar. I got whistled at a lot which was flattering and I was invited out by both locals and summer visitors but I always refused. I was still traumatised by what had happened to me. I believed myself to be still in love with Hal and I was unable to trust any man again. In addition, none of the men asking me on a date even minimally attracted me. One late Saturday afternoon, the landlord of The Spinning Knight came into the kitchen where his wife and I were preparing a fiddly strawberry meringue for the evening dessert. "Sian", he said, "there was a fellow in here yesterday evening asking for you. Said he knew you when you worked at the Glaisfar. I think he mentioned something about buying that piece of land your family owns. I told him where you lived. Did he come round?"

"No", I replied slightly surprised, wondering who it could be. I assumed Iris must have given the individual in question our address but it was a pointless exercise anyway as the field was willed between my mother and Theodore and the latter was adamant about not selling. My grandmother would have sold it tomorrow in order to buy Davy Cottage from Sir Rob who had offered it to her at a reasonable price because she was a sitting tenant. But Theodore was not keen and he was holding the purse strings. Time and again did my mother and grandmother discuss the potential sale of the land (they were capable of holding long conversations on this topic if nothing else) and formulated schemes to convince Theodore of the advantages of the sale but so far they had been unsuccessful. On my return home I mentioned the potential buyer to my mother who immediately looked interested. My mother's mood was now more stable as she had not consumed alcohol for some years. However, when anxious she tended to take more Valium than prescribed and at times her speech was so slurred that some of the villagers still believed she was drinking. Since her discharge from hospital, our relationship had improved. It would never be close as there was far too much water under too many bridges and my grandmother had always been in the role of my support and mainstay. My mother had constantly hurt and saddened me so I found it easier to push her away emotionally than to face continuing disappointment and frustration by her addiction and irrational behaviour. But in spite of this, our relationship was better than it had ever been before.

One rainy Saturday afternoon after serving lunch to the guests at The Spinning Knight, I picked my way across the unevenly tarmacked pub car park with umbrella held aloft, trying to dodge the June downpour and the rapidly engulfing puddles. I was carrying four large freshly laid eggs in a brown paper bag that the landlord had kindly sent for my family. Out of the corner of my eye, I spied a man in an impressive car parked discreetly near the exit. As I passed he suddenly flung open his car door and called out "Sian". I approached the car hesitantly, the teeming rain obscuring the driver from view but at some level of awareness I felt I knew his voice. I suddenly found my looking into the cornflower blue eyes of Harold Stanton. "Sian, please get in the car, I need to talk to you". I looked at him in shock and amazement, unable to comprehend his presence, my long hair dripping rivulets down the back of my neck and on to my fashionable Dannimac. I had waited for nearly a year for some word or contact but as each day passed and none came I had gradually reconciled myself to his loss and to his final rejection of me. So reconciled was I that it never occurred to me that the landlord of The Spinning Knight might be referring to Harold Stanton when he told me about the person enquiring after me. Six months ago, I would have seized the hope it would be him and waited with trepidation every day that passed for him to make contact. On this occasion, the least likely and unconsidered hypothesis was that the interested party referred to might be Hal - although I had told him in the past about our piece of land.

"Get in Sian, you are soaking wet," he said impatiently. "Shut the car door."

I got into the car, used to obeying his commands. I sat silently unable to say anything, completely lost for words. Hal spoke first, but I couldn't help noticing that he sounded a little embarrassed and that the usual smooth confidence had gone.

"Sian, I had to see you to tell you that I'm so very sorry for what happened."

There was silence and then I heard myself say:

"Oh, forget it Hal, it's all part of growing up. So why are you here? Back in South Wales and looking for another teenage mistress?"

"Good God, what's got into you?" He sounded shocked and indignant. He then calmed down and put his hand on my arm.

"I'm not back working here permanently. I come down very occasionally to complete some bits of my previous contract with Welsh Valley Industries that didn't get finished. I'm not staying at the Glaisfar this time but at a small hotel close to the site where I work. It's a diabolical place".

"I'm really sorry for you, Hal".

"Oh, for Godsake Sian, hear me out. I'm sorry I didn't contact you before but there was a reason.... he hesitated and lowered his voice.

"Yes, I know. Your wife was pregnant at the same time. Iris told me".

This threw him off guard and I had the satisfaction of seeing him flounder for words. Hal Stanton was never at a loss for words.

"Yeah, yeah.... that's true. It's a long story... but it's not that I was going to say. The reason I didn't contact you was I promised Dr Klein that I wouldn't."

I sat in silence feeling a strange sensation of being out of my body and watching the scene as an observer. I felt as if I was floating in a dream and wondered when I would wake up and become conscious.

"Dr Klein. Dr Klein told you not to have any further contact with me?"

"Yes. And he would have made life very difficult for me if I had broken my word".

"You could have written Hal, or you could have told me about your promise to Dr Klein a year ago. I would have accepted it. All these months... my throat was choked with a surge of overwhelming emotion and streaming tears began to join the rain coursing down my wet face.

Hal pulled me towards him and gently dried my eyes. Suddenly I felt his lips on mine and he kissed me in his old familiar way.

"I really care about you Sian. I couldn't stand it anymore, that's why I came to find you. I am so very sorry".

As his body touched mine, I was galvanised into action by the trauma of my emotional state. I sat up suddenly and pushed him away.

"You bastard!", I said. " Dr Klein may have told you not to continue your affair with a seventeen-year-old girl but he wasn't the reason you never wrote a single letter to me. No, you were afraid that if something went wrong with the actual abortion or afterwards...as there was a possibility it could, you would leave some written evidence behind you and that may well have affected your career and your marriage. I am not as green as I was, Hal. I will never forget the time of the abortion. The whole thing was so seedy and sordid and I needed you so much then. What would I have done without my two wonderful friends who really do care for me? Let me out of this bloody car."

He bent forward as if to open the car door. His face was pale and I noticed an expression I'd never seen before; I recognised it as shame.

My anger was so overwhelming that I thought I'd explode. Not only had he acted like a total bastard but he attempted to put the blame for his actions on Dr Klein who had been the only adult person willing to help me, albeit with some reservation. I was shaking with rage as I got out of the car. Hal leaned towards me to say something but before he did, I lifted up the brown paper bag with the freshly laid eggs and banged them down on his head before slamming the door on his shouts of angry indignation. "Go to hell!", I shouted.

I rushed back to Davy Cottage and flung open the door. My grandmother was in the kitchen giving my mother instructions for making an apple tart. She was sitting in my grandfather's worn leather chair by the lead grate fire as she easily tired these days. She was seventy-eight and her failing physical health prohibited her carrying out her usual domestic chores. I pushed these intrusive thoughts away and continued to deny her illness up until the very end. They both looked up suddenly as I burst in dripping wet and my grandmother said, "Good Lord Sian! You look as if you have seen a ghost!".

"I did Gran, but a living ghost. Oh, I've proved Grandpa's theory about having more to fear from the living than the dead. Give me the living any day, you can tell them to bugger off!"

Leaving them both in total bewilderment by my vocabulary, I went to my bedroom to change my clothes and dry my hair. As I sat on the bed with my new pink hairdryer, it suddenly occurred to me that in all the reunions with Hal Stanton that I had fantasised and dreamed about over the past year, not one had come within a striking distance of present reality. I thought of Hal sitting in his expensive car, wearing a smart white trench coat with four smashed fresh eggs dripping down his forehead and onto his collar. I wondered how he would explain that one but knowing Hal, he'd find a way. I hooted with laughter, rolling about on the bed, my merriment in stiff competition with overriding feelings of suffused pain and anger. But I had a vague premonition that I had not seen the last of Harold Stanton.

Chapter 9

Music: *"The Sound of Silence".* Simon and Garfunkel (1964)

Anna's experience of her Independent School in Cardiff was significantly negative. It was the first time she had encountered anti-Semitism and hostility from her fellow students and from some teachers. The school was single-sex and by examination admission only. Scholarships were offered to children from financially disadvantaged backgrounds but there were few of them. In the main, the school served a prosperous middle-class community and was conveniently situated in one of the better areas of the city. There were more Jewish girls at the school than there had been at Foistneth Grammar but there was only one in Anna's form, a girl called Ruby Weiz. Ruby's mother had converted to Judaism after Ruby was born so when this was discussed at home, Juliet ventured her opinion that Anna needed to discuss Ruby's claim to Jewish legitimacy with a Rabbi. Anna retorted sharply that she had so much studying to do and not enough time to do it and that entering into a discussion with their Rabbi on the Jewish authenticity of Ruby Weiz's parentage was by no means a priority for her and 'the whole Jewish thing was a lot of nonsense anyway'. This usually provoked an angry reaction in Juliet who would accuse her daughter of "betraying your cultural traditions and denying your grandparents who perished in the Holocaust." Anna's father would then be called in to mediate and correct Anna's manners.

The main stumbling block for Anna was that she had joined the school at sixteen whereas her classmates had been there since the age of eleven. Anna was very much the outsider new girl. She had no hope of inclusion with the 'in crowd' as that group of self-confident girls tended to ignore her or sometimes openly mock her odd clothes and lack of modern dress sense. School uniform was not compulsory for sixth form pupils except for formal school events such as prize-giving or a visit from a local dignitary. Miniskirts were the fashion of the day and some girls were intent on seeing how far they could push the teachers' boundaries on tolerance and decorum. But Juliet Klein always insisted that Anna's skirts unfashionably trailed well below the knee and all jumpers or tops left no skin exposed. It was as if Juliet was making up for her lost Jewish mores in the Foistneth era and as a consequence it became crucial to adopt the outer trappings of orthodox Judaism with a rigid and uncompromising attitude. Trying to obey Jewish dietary laws and Jewish tradition had been an on-going battle for Juliet. She did not drive and she had always been reliant on her busy GP husband to collect her food shopping by car. Now she could shop on foot or have it delivered. There were two kosher butchers in her own area as well as a Jewish delicatessen that sold Vienna sausage and soused herring. Although pleased for her mother, Anna could not see what all the fuss was about and said that eating kosher food would hardly make her a better person.

"It is not only about the food although the Torah (Old Testament) clearly states what a Jew can and cannot eat," Juliet would snap. "It is about Jewish identity. What makes a Jew different?" Anna dared not argue with her mother on this topic for too long without potential repercussions.

At school Anna was known as 'the thin Jewess' with Ruby Weiz taking the title of 'the fat Jewess'. Anna refused to be intimidated and seethed with rage when she overheard some of the muttered insults aimed from her fellow pupils. One of the most popular stereotype was about how Shakespeare got it right when it came to "grasping Jews taking other people's money". Outwardly she kept her calm, with the exception of her quivering voice, as she attempted to tackle the anti-Semitic offenders in argument. But the offenders were weak at discussion and tended to avoid it by walking off with a contemptuous shrug of the shoulders. Only two other girls in Anna's form were studying sciences and Anna found the two to be less judgmental than her fellow Arts students that formed the core of the 'in crowd'. Nevertheless, Anna experienced both 'science girls' as very boring and she found it difficult to relate to either of them. Because of this, she and Ruby Weiz ended up spending a lot of time together, mainly because of the Jewish connection, but also because Ruby was not in Anna's category academically and was very reliant on her new friend's support with her schoolwork. Ruby said she hoped to marry soon after she had completed her education and have lots of children. Anna did not share Ruby's future ambition and was determined to go to university as far away from her parents as possible. Nevertheless, she felt very guilty when such thoughts stormed through her mind and intruded into her consciousness.

At the local Orthodox synagogue there were a number of young women and men Anna's age but she felt an outsider even there for a while. Everyone seemed to know one another. But unlike her school, Anna was made welcome and she began to feel a sense of cultural belonging through the Hebrew religious service, Jewish music and predominantly through the various activities she sometimes attended at the synagogue during the week. Anna joined the Zionist Youth group and developed a keen interest in what was happening in Israel. Juliet was in charge of her children's Jewish education and her sons complied without too much difficulty. Myron was only eight years old and he was learning Hebrew at the synagogue Cheder (Sunday School) and Lawrence also attended sometimes. During this period, Anna began to learn modern Hebrew at evening classes. Within Orthodox Judaism, it was less important for girls to learn Hebrew as they were not called up to read from the Torah scrolls or actively participate in the religious service. The role of the Jewish woman was perceived predominantly as that of homemaker. Juliet would light candles on 'Shabbat' every Friday evening at sunset and say the candle blessing in Hebrew. She had started to consistently follow religious rituals after their move to Cardiff. Sometimes Anna draped a chiffon scarf over her head and said the Friday night candle blessing in Hebrew. She liked doing this as it gave her mother pleasure but in a strange way, it helped her feel emotionally grounded and gave her a sense of identity with the wider Jewish community.

But at school things went from bad to worse. In addition, Anna found herself struggling with her chemistry A Level and realised she was not good enough for even a pass. She was good at maths, excelled at biology and could just about manage physics if she worked hard, but chemistry defeated her and caused her many sleepless nights. In her second year, Dr Klein engaged a chemistry tutor but by then Anna had lost a lot of unrecoverable ground and both Anna and the tutor acknowledged that her pass grade in chemistry was likely to be low.

Anna also feared that she may only score a 'C' in physics which would not be enough to get her into medical school. She worked harder and harder but was dismayed when she felt she was losing her habitual learning pace and that her parents would be so disappointed if she failed. It became apparent to those around Anna, including the family cleaner, that she was drastically losing weight and becoming more and more reclusive. Her father sometimes commented on her thinness but his comments made Anna angry and defensive so Juliet asked him to refrain from mentioning her weight as "all young girls are either underweight or overweight". Harry Klein promptly rejected this statement saying, "who's the doctor in this house?" But Anna continued to lose weight. She also started to vomit up her food and use laxatives on a regular basis, unbeknown to her parents. Anna believed unconditionally that she was putting on weight and making herself even uglier. On one occasion Juliet caught Anna coming out of the lavatory with a flushed face and carrying her small wireless. "What are you doing?" she questioned. "Are you being sick again?

"I'm fine", retorted Anna sharply. "Why do you keep picking on me all the time?"

She scurried into her bedroom and slammed the door, refusing to answer her mother's pleas to open the door and talk. Juliet expressed her concerns to her husband but he maintained that her bizarre behaviour was probably due to her imminent examinations and that she was under a lot of pressure at school. Juliet actively encouraged young Jewish men and women from the synagogue to come to the family home, including the 'questionably Jewish' Ruby Weiz. Ruby immediately found herself a mate, much to Juliet's annoyance, but Anna showed little interest in anyone, male or female. She mourned the loss of her friends, Pearl and Sian, and no one else could come close as a substitute. Anna's physical and mental health continued to deteriorate and after her A Level examinations were finally completed, she weighed just under six stone; she was 5 ft. 5 inches in height.

Anna had three interviews for medical school, two in London and one in Leicester. Her getting a place was contingent on her getting through the interview as well as on her examination performance. Her exam results were finally released and her last and final interview was held at

St. George's Hospital in South London where her low weight was commented on by one of the male interviewers with a reference to the stamina needed by junior doctors. Anna retorted sharply saying that she could eat absolutely anything but always ended up losing weight rather than gaining it. The interview panel was not convinced and had every reason to prove their theory as medical professionals. On her return home to Cardiff after her last interview, Anna collapsed on Paddington Station and was immediately rushed to St. Mary's Hospital and put on a glucose drip. She was eventually given a diagnosis of anorexia nervosa. Anna now weighed little more than five stone and fine downy hair had begun to appear on both her face and arms. Dr Klein was informed the same evening and he arrived at the hospital the following day but without his wife as it was too short notice to make arrangements to leave Lawrence and Myron. Juliet would follow within a few days. As Dr Klein sat by his daughter's bed, he silently prayed she would recover and blamed himself for pressurising his daughter towards medicine when perhaps she would have been happier doing something else. Anna was extremely good at art but she had been encouraged to drop the subject for A Level as painting was 'a hobby that led nowhere unless you were a Monet or a Picasso'. Anna had been so upset when he insisted she drop art in order to concentrate on her science subjects but she had passively accepted her father's advice. She did not know how not to as she always had complied academically with her parents' wishes. Struggling with his conscience, Harry Klein faced the harsh reality that he had expected too much of his daughter and that he had put his own needs ahead of hers. He had known for two years that Anna was unhappy at her school but he had insisted she stay there as it was "an excellent school with many advantages." He had wanted only the best for her, a good lifestyle and academic excellence worthy of his child but was this the price she had to pay? Was it worth it? Looking at his rake thin daughter with protruding bones not dissimilar to a Holocaust survivor lying in a hospital bed and attached to a saline drip, he wondered now what these advantages were. Had he and Juliet escaped Nazi persecution only to irretrievably damage their own children physically and mentally by being over-zealous in their ambition for them? Harry vowed that night that if Anna survived he would make no more demands on her. He would give her the choice to do what she wished academically and allow her to reject medical school if that is what she wanted. Harry heard himself 'bargaining with God' but he did not know what else he could do. He sat with his face in his hands. One of the nurses brought him a cup of tea and clipped a new bag of glucose water to the drip. Anna opened her eyes slowly.

"Papa. What happened to me?"

"Anna, Anna what have you done to yourself? What have you done? Oh my God, my God! Your mother will be here soon, child," he said soothingly, patting his daughter's arm. Privately he feared Anna might deteriorate before Juliet's arrival. Dr Klein cursed his wife's over-protectiveness of her sons.

"I feel an ugly Jewess".

"Anna child, who has been saying these things. Who?"

"Everybody - except for Sian and Pearl."

Anna survived, just. She remained in the hospital in London for fourteen weeks and she was seen weekly by a psychiatrist and twice weekly by a psychotherapist. She began to put on weight and was released when her target weight was reached but equally importantly, when both she and her family began to consider making some important changes to their lifestyle. Anna's second cousins from Northwest London visited almost every day and Joe the Dentist came up with the idea of Anna having 'a year out' and giving herself the option of medical school the following year. She had been accepted by the University of London after all, in spite of a C in chemistry. She had gained A grades in both biology and physics and a B grade in maths. Joe suggested a trip to Israel to stay with Harry Klein's brother and his family. Anna was enthusiastic but Juliet disapproved, saying there too many political problems with the Palestinians in Israel and it could be dangerous. Nevertheless, Harry insisted knowing how involved Anna was in Youth Aliyah (Zionist Youth Movement) supporting many of Israel's projects in social welfare, health and education. He maintained the sunny climate of Israel would help Anna to recuperate both physically and mentally from her illness and she would consolidate her Jewish roots within her own extended family.

Anna departed for Israel at the end of September 1964, two days after Rosh Hashanah, the Jewish New Year.

CHAPTER 10

Music: *'Hatikvah' ('The Hope')*. Enrico Macias

Tel Aviv January 1965

Hello both of you.

I will be sending two copies of the same letter separately but I thought I would address it to both of you.

I'm really sorry we lost touch over the past year but I have been ill with an illness called anorexia nervosa, i.e., an eating disorder where I attempted to starve myself to death. I know it sounds dramatic - most unlike me - but I was on a saline drip for ten days at a London hospital and they told me I had been depressed for months. I finally got into Med. School but I was only offered a place by one university (London) - albeit an excellent one - so I didn't do so brilliantly after all!

I have heard you will be leaving for University College London, Sian. Congratulations at getting a place on the language course! And Pearl, I hope you are enjoying your new job in Oxford. I'm sorry I was unable to contact you before I left but my parents were against the idea as they always think you two will lead me astray! Considering what we three have been through together, their concern is not unreasonable. Oh, the Beatles music is all the rage here, by the way, I thought I'd let you know.

I have never been so happy in my whole life. I really have found something wonderful here. It is so hard to describe the beauty of Israel. I can only tell you how I feel about it, hopefully without too much sentimentality. I flew from Heathrow on EL AL Airlines. The journey took nearly eight hours and we re-fuelled in Ankara. As we were coming into land at Ben-Gurion Airport, the Israeli Anthem, the Hatikvah (The Hope) was played over the intercom. People were clapping their hands and shouting for joy whilst others were crying with joy and happiness. Their elation was sucked into my heart and made me feel part of something -

something important. I was one of them; I belong.

What amazed me when I got off the aeroplane was the brilliance of the blue sky and stark whiteness of the buildings. It looks a bit barren after Britain but nevertheless parts of Israel are very green with lush lands full of trees and vegetation. There are eucalyptus trees and cypresses and citrus trees everywhere. Oh, the heat! You have no idea. I'm not used to this and it is by no means the hottest time of the year. What will I do in August?

My Uncle Bibi and his wife Sonja have a spacious apartment in the middle of Tel Aviv. Two of my cousins are still living at home. Their daughter Rifka is two years older than me and Soshana is a year younger. They have a large circle of friends so I believe we will have some fun. You know, people are Jewish here and don't have to prove anything by going to a 'mikveh' - remember that ritual bath thing I told you about where Jewish women go before they get married and every time after their period? They are not concerned about eating fish that have neither scales nor fins and my aunt served us prawns for lunch the other day! My mother used to drive me crazy with these things and put me right off Judaism altogether. It's fun here, because much of the religious ritual is meant to celebrate a happy occasion, and it is not soused in pickled herrings and gloom as Diaspora Jews portray it. However, I sympathise with the reasons and am aware that because we are a minority culture in Great Britain with European parents who escaped the Holocaust, traditional rituals common to the home country bind us together and give us a sense of a shared identity. But I question whether we go too far with it all. Which reminds me, in my class at that horrendous snobby school in Cardiff was a Jewish girl called Ruby Weiz. Her father's Jewish but her mother only converted to Judaism about two years ago. The point is that she hadn't converted when Ruby was born. Joseph Weiz is a big donor to the Shul so the Rabbi isn't too bothered about Ruby's heritage as she was brought up Jewish anyway. My mother is angry about this saying she will write to the Chief Rabbi because any gullible Jewish man might marry Ruby and then find out she is not really Jewish at all and their children cannot claim to be Jewish and they will be stateless in

Israel! Here in Israel, people appear to have conversations about things that matter. So many people talk of the execution two years ago of Adolf Eichmann. You remember, he organised Hitler's Nazi extermination programme. There is also much speculation about a conspiracy surrounding the assassination of President Kennedy as it is highly unlikely that Lee Harvey Oswald could have carried out the assassination of the president alone. But what are we discussing at home? The Jewish authenticity of Ruby Weiz and her mother! Oh, I had better get off this topic because it makes me so angry!

I will be working on a Kibbutz in Tel Aviv, looking after some of the smaller children and working in the kitchen sometimes. I know you two have experienced praiseworthy manual labour but I never have, being an academic with servants -if you can call Mrs Meredith, our daily, 'a servant'. Here people really work hard on the kibbutzim to contribute to the wealth and social development of the country. I am happy to do it as my life's been relatively easy compared to many here. By the way, I've started to learn Hebrew again as a good 70% of the population speak it. Some people here speak Yiddish but I only know a few words as my parents never spoke it. Others speak Ladino - a kind of Judaeo-Spanish. By the way, the food is fantastic! I don't think I ever would ever have become anorexic in Israel! Yes, I know I shouldn't joke about it. There are magnificent fresh fruit juices to have for breakfast with local goats' cheese, olives, eggs, delicate pastries and various Israeli dairy specialities. My uncle took us to some lovely beaches in Tel Aviv (I sound like 'Glyn the Gatehouse', don't I?) and people spend a lot of time outdoors, shopping at markets or picnicking on beaches. The Israelis come over as very abrupt and sometimes rude but American settlers are really great. There's never a boring moment!

That's all for now. Will write again soon.

Love and best wishes

Anna.

Letter 2; May 1965

Hello both. Thanks for your letters. Sorry to hear the Halls of Residence are so diabolical, Sian. I think it's a good idea for you two to find some decent accommodation together this summer. You work for an accommodation bureau in London now, don't you Pearl? It shouldn't be too difficult.

My whole family left Israel for England last Tuesday. They were here three weeks and they all had a wonderful time, especially Lawrence. I didn't realise how much I really miss them but I definitely do not want to return to England. I don't want to go to medical school but I haven't told my father yet!!! Instead, I am considering switching to psychology and doing my degree in the USA. Oh, you gasp! Where did this idea come from and how are you going to do it? Well, as I told you in my last letter, I am working on a kibbutz with young children and I have become fascinated by theories of developmental psychology. I have spoken to adult children of Holocaust survivors and much of what they say regarding their parents' - particularly their mothers' treatment of them - is so familiar to me. My mother is not technically a Holocaust survivor as she was not interned in a concentration camp but all her family were murdered in death camps in Poland. Many children of Holocaust survivors I know say there is a tendency among the parents to repress the past and cancel it from daily memory. But past memories - whether images, words or smells re-surface regardless of repression and some survivors have become violent and abusive towards their children, whilst others are cold, withdrawn and psychologically rejecting. Many say that their mothers would prefer to spend time discussing their physical rather than mental health as emotions are taboo. I certainly identify with that in our family! Jews had to repress any emotion under the Nazi regime at the cost of individual survival. Because of their appalling trauma and unimaginable experiences, there is the tendency of many parents to minimise their children's suffering as they perceive it as minor compared to their own in the concentration camp. Of course, one would agree that the suffering of their own children is on a very different scale to theirs but it is no less painful and real. Our parents make us feel guilty for complaining about anything because we have food and shelter and no one is threatening us with deportation. You know, my mother could not talk about my feelings and what led me to self-starvation but I knew she believed me ungrateful when her own parents and siblings had been beaten, starved and tortured in Auschwitz. I wish I could change things for her but I can't. I can only change the way I see things. As you have probably guessed from this (I doubt it though), I am undergoing psychotherapy with an American psychoanalyst. She is helping me face some of my own demons and I get very upset sometimes in therapy but I know I need to continue with it.

Went to Jerusalem with my family the week after they arrived and we visited the Western Wall which is the last standing vestige of Herod's temple compound and Jerusalem's holiest site. We were all overcome by it although only men are allowed to pray there so my father went alone and we went to the women's section. Later on that day we went into the Negev and experienced the most fabulous of sunsets.

Now, listen to this: I am in love and having 'a real love affair' with an American - Israeli archaeologist. He is called Yossi Tamir. It was he who suggested I go to the States and study what interests ME *rather than what interests my father. It was suggested I attend Boston University School of Medicine and study psychology there. I know my father will be bitterly disappointed but I do not want to be a doctor. I am more interested in people's minds than their physical illnesses and even if I opted for psychiatry, I would still need to do a medical training. I really do not want to do this. I am a coward; I could not tell my father when he was here. I believe I could get permission to study in the USA as we have relatives there but.... Anyway, Yossi is FANTASTIC! He's six years older than me and single so I will join Sian's club for older men! He is encouraging me in my career and is far more interesting than the boys I have met up till now. Yes, I'm taking 'precautions'. I'd be a fool not to after what I experienced second-hand with you, Sian. Must rush as am going out for the evening with my cousins.*

Will let you know soon whether I am robust enough mentally to weather the storm at home and not return. Some days I feel really good about it but other days I lose total confidence in myself. Need to discuss it with my therapist.

Love and best wishes and take care both.

Your loving friend

Anna

PART II

ADULTHOOD: THE NINETEEN SEVENTIES AND BEYOND

Chapter 11

Music: *'Midnight Cowboy'*, John Barry (1969)

On my second year at London University, I switched from the study of French to the study of Italian. It was a momentous decision and no mean feat, starting from scratch with a language I did not know. I was keen to do it because Italy was the country I most wanted to visit and it had an enchanting history of Renaissance art and literature that I found enthralling. The diverse fields of knowledge and experience propagated by University life was expanding and I found my chosen area of study highly stimulating much of the time. A significant drawback was financial insecurity. I wanted to experience Italy in person but I needed to work during the vacations when my university grant was abruptly terminated. I worked in bars and hotels in central London during my first and second years at University. I even worked briefly as a cocktail waitress at the Playboy Club on Piccadilly complete with bunny tail and fishnet stockings but I was not fast enough at toting up orders and reacted acerbically when a drunken customer attempted to paw me. I told him he could order a drink and discuss the weather and the state of the nation all he pleased but he had no right to disrespect the waitress by fondling her private parts, regardless of whether she was dressed for office work or undressed as a Bunny Girl. Needless to say, I was fired by the management after barely three weeks.

Pearl moved out of our shared accommodation on my final year at University. We had lived together in a three-bedroom flat in Maida Vale for fourteen months. The other flat mate was a girl from Slough called Diane Watson and she was engaged to Neil Haines from Chislehurst. The couple were noisy love makers causing Pearl and myself some merriment as we couldn't help overhearing the squeaks of their rusty bedsprings whenever they were in the mood for lust. Neil caused us some major irritation as he tended to hang around Diane at weekends when she didn't return to Slough and gobble our yoghurts from the fridge.

Pearl was currently dating a man called Kevin whom she had met at Flatfinders. Kevin was a rare breed: a twenty-three-year-old authentic Londoner from Forest Hill working North of the River. Kevin vaguely resembled the pop star Adam Faith in appearance, a great favourite of Pearl's as a teenager. Kevin was bright and dynamic with a thousand and one business schemes on the go at any one time. They were sleeping together but he rarely stayed over at our flat in Maida Vale, preferring Pearl to stay at his newly mortgaged property in Forest Hill. She usually did this at weekends so sometimes I had the flat to myself. I too had 'a sort of boyfriend', a fellow student with a steady girlfriend at a Northern university. We had slept together a couple of times when inebriated but although I liked Alan, he was not my type being a little too intellectual and obsessive about the campaign for nuclear disarmament (CND). I half-heartedly went along to a few London rallies with him but I found many of the speakers annoying, their words jarred by a cacophony of extra-loud megaphones. The best part of the rally was getting drunk on cheap beer afterwards with dogged conversations on political and social change until the early hours of the morning rounded off by a shared cannabis joint. This was a million light years away from the demeaning 1950's attitude to women and the subtle sleaze of the Playboy Club camouflaged so tastefully beneath a cloak of wealth, elegance, and ostensible respectability.

I was not unwilling to share Alan with the girl from the North as he flattered me by saying I was prettier than his girlfriend Lucy even if less committed to CND than she was. I knew our relationship would not last because of our diverse interests and the lack of sexual chemistry between us.

One Friday afternoon in May, on my return home from Senate House Library, I pushed my way off the Circle Line, tearing up the stairs at Baker Street in the direction of the Bakerloo Line tube. As I stopped hurriedly to buy a copy of the 'Evening News', I became aware of a man standing next to me fishing in his pocket for change. I did a double take as my brain struggled to merge a number of juxtaposed and familiar images. It was uncanny but I was almost certain that the person I was seeing was Hal Stanton but there was doubt as I could only briefly see the outline of his profile as he scurried down the steps leading to the Metropolitan Line. He was wearing a dark suit and carried an expensive calf leather briefcase. The height and build were undeniably his but my mind was in turmoil as I followed him in the direction of the Metropolitan Line, debating yet again whether it really was him and if it was, what should I do. Here fate hovered ominously overhead, holding my life in the balance but with the tantalising option of choice. If I'd decided to walk away - too self-conscious to establish the passenger's identity - then my life would probably have been lived very differently. My actions sealed both our destinies on the Baker Street platform that day. A loud train approached with a screech of brakes, expelling gusts of air over the waiting passengers. I was aware that unless I seized my chance now, it was highly unlikely that there would ever present another opportunity like this in a city of seven million people.

With a shaking voice I called out loudly "Hal!". He swung around and our eyes locked. It was him.

"Sian", he said incredulously. "Is it really you? He appeared nonplussed by my sudden appearance. What are you doing here?"

"I live in London now. I'm studying languages at the University of London". He drew a sharp intake of breath as he stared at me bewildered. Suddenly, he plonked his briefcase down on the floor of the platform, at the same time impulsively throwing his arms around me, to the annoyance of desperate commuters trying to push past onto the train in order to avoid standing all the way to Watford. Crackling incoherent announcements in thick Cockney accents permeated across the general clamour of the station mentioning train delays and ordering us to stand clear of the doors and let other passengers off first. Hal took charge, as he always had done.

"Come on, let's go and have a coffee. I'll catch a later train."

We went to the one and only coffee bar on Baker Street Station and sat on uncomfortable backless stools at the counter. Hal updated me on the current events in his life. He had changed his job and was working for an engineering company and the head office was in Baker Street. He usually visited the office a couple of times in a week. He, Julia and their two children had moved to Watford. Elizabeth was five and their son Alexander was three; the age my child would have been if it had been allowed to live. I think both of us were aware of what was between us when he showed me, at my request, a photograph of his two children. I was relieved, for some unfathomable reason, that Julia was not in the photograph.

Hal asked about my family and friends as well as my university course. I told him I was highly stimulated by my course and that I had managed top A. level grades for university entry. I also told him that I was relieved and happy to finally leave home for good. I wittered on about Pearl and Kevin and the strained relationships between our flat sharers. Then an instinctive need made me open up and mention my grandmother who had died last year of stomach cancer. She was removed from home to Foistneth General Hospital where she died after nearly three weeks of agonising pain. I had already arrived at Davy Cottage when they admitted her because my mother had written to me in London saying she was deteriorating fast but the new village doctor had been unable to convince her to accept a hospital bed. My mother begged me to come home believing I had more influence with my grandmother than she did. When my grandmother finally accepted hospitalisation, she was in far too much physical pain to care where she was. We visited almost daily and Theo collected us a few times a week from the hospital. Other times we came and went with Wales Fargo. When she was partly lucid, I was sure she recognised me and she smiled contentedly when I squeezed her limp and wrinkled hand.

"Gran, it's me, Sian".

"Sian", she responded weakly, "so pleased, Sian, so pleased you are doing well at school". She had always been slim with a bony frame but her metamorphosis was terrifying; her frame was skeletal as she gradually wasted away. Her translucent skin had a greyish hue; her sharp grey eyes usually so intent on what was happening around her, had lost their spark to a dulled expression. The morphine was clouding her thoughts and playing havoc with her memory but at least she was aware of who I was. I thanked God for that as I sat at her bedside, fighting with the desire to cry my heart out. I had not done my best by her. I had been too self-centred and too focussed on myself and my overwhelming need to leave South Wales. I had not reflected enough on how much she loved me and the many sacrifices she had made on my behalf.

I will always regret that I was not with her when she died. My mother had suggested a cup of tea and so I went to the kitchen to ask one of the nurses and this had taken longer than it should have. There were three other elderly people on the ward and on my return I noticed the curtains were drawn around my grandmother's bed. Advancing with some bewilderment, I was suddenly met by a young nurse who whispered: "she's just gone, Sian". My mother was sitting at my grandmother's bedside looking blank, holding my grandmother's hand. My grandmother was so still but her expression had lost its pain contortions of the past days. She was staring upwards, her eyes open, her skin the colour of alabaster. She had finally found peace, at least I liked to think so. I kissed her on the forehead and her skin was still warm.

My grandmother was buried with my grandfather at the Chapel although she had made it plain that she disliked Welsh Baptists and wanted to be buried in the churchyard of the village. Theodore said it was impractical as they had a plot in the chapel cemetery not at the church where the village rector was "a fussy so and so" and a stickler for burial protocol. Theodore said it would be expensive to bury her somewhere else and in any case, "a wife's place is with her husband". I tried to persuade him as tactfully as I could: "You know she disliked the chapel and did not want to be buried there."

"She'll go where she's put", rebuffed Theodore with an air of finality.

For once my mother agreed with Theodore so there was little I could do either by emotional argument or financial persuasion.

"What does it matter where you are when you dead?" mouthed my mother grabbing two Valium tablets from the bottle, "I know I wouldn't care."

"Stay with me Gran", I prayed silently at the funeral. I cried a lot before, during and after the funeral. My mother had chosen two tear-jerking hymns called 'Jesu Lover of My Soul' and 'Lead Kindly Light' both of which my grandmother profoundly disliked. This was Alice's unconscious way of getting even. My mother squeezed out a few tears on the day of the funeral, but her refuge from emotional distress continued to be her Valium. Out of respect for my grandmother and village decorum, Mattie Boyce did not attend the funeral. Anna did not attend either as she was in the USA but Pearl took a day off work and Theo collected her from the station at Foistneth after picking up Dora from the café. Wilf was unwell on this occasion and unable to attend. Theodore asked me to pay him ' the petrol money' for fetching Pearl even though he was full time employed and I was a student. One thing I learned; people rarely change. Theodore was tight-fisted as a child and just as tight-fisted as an adult. I left the village after the funeral and at the same time as Pearl so as not to run up yet another petrol bill with Theodore. A neighbour offered to provide a funeral spread for the mourners maintaining that someone had to do it as "the men will be hungry". Neither I nor my mother were capable of organising this sort of formal occasion. My mother irritated me with her inane remarks about other mourners and we were always on the verge of having arguments. I couldn't wait to get away. Dora wept loudly throughout the service annoying Pearl and myself as we both knew she disliked my grandmother. The chapel was packed to the rafters with people. My Grandmother barely knew any of them but had always said that many would come to to gawp as they had at her husband's funeral and she had little patience with any of them. For once the rain held off and after the gloomy Baptist service, my grandmother's coffin was gently laid to rest in the grave of her despised husband. All of a sudden, I caught a glimpse of Dora lighting a cigarette while she was chatting away to Tim the Deacon. I was amazed to see her inadvertently flick some cigarette ash into the newly dug open grave. No doubt it landed on the white rose redolent with perfume that I had thrown onto my grandmother's coffin barely minutes before. Years later, we three laughed long and hard about this, but it angered me greatly at the time.

Hal did not mention our last meeting in Wales and the crushed eggs on his head. He looked as handsome as ever but a little more tired and lined than I remembered. We exchanged telephone numbers and he agreed to call me next time he was at head office. Part of me did not expect to see him again but he called within three weeks and we went to a trendy Indian restaurant in Ladbroke Grove. During dinner I asked him what time his last train was to Watford but he winked and said he'd got the key for the company apartment in Baker Street. He said it was used by company executives and senior staff needing overnight accommodation in London and it was cheaper for the company than using hotels. I reacted with an unanticipated surge of anger deep down in my gut.

"Do you think I am going to sleep with you because you have bought me dinner, Hal? Have you moved out of the 1950s yet?"

He scowled and looked uncomfortable.

"That's a tactless thing to say. I meant we could go back there for a nightcap after dinner. I had to take the key, just in case we were served dinner late and I missed the last train back. You can take a taxi home from there if you don't want to stay."

But I did not take a taxi. We purchased a bottle of wine and returned to the clean and comfortable one-bedroom flat in a purpose-built block just off Baker Street. The flat was on the third floor. I have memories of a red carpet spanning the corridor floor and a heavy gold framed mirror hanging close to the auspicious apartment '33'. We let ourselves in without any difficulty and took off our jackets. Hal searched for wine glasses whilst I headed for the bathroom. I then went into the bedroom, removed my shoes and lay down on the double bed, my toes pointing towards the ceiling. I could see the gentle shadow of the dying sun as it sank into the clouds over the horizon and then out of sight. Hal arrived with the glasses of wine and put them down on the bedside table. He sat next to me on the double bed, facing sideways. He suddenly leaned forward and gently kissed me on the lips.

"I thought we weren't going to do this", he whispered.

I sat up and slowly, in front of him, I removed my tights and underwear still looking into his eyes. "I think we are", I replied. "I know I want to".

He moved down swiftly on top of me. "My God, Sian," he groaned. Then he lifted his head said quickly, "What about precautions? We don't want..."

"It's okay. I'm on the pill this time".

Sex with Hal was so exciting and we both reached orgasm quickly. We fell asleep and when I woke in the night he was caressing me and we made love again. I found it hard to believe how different this was to my lack lustre forays with Alan. We both agreed we needed to be together again, even if only for fleeting encounters. I was committed to visiting Italy in June with the hope of attaining a Reader post at one of the

Italian universities. I eventually took a Readership at the University of Catania in Sicily and left indefinitely for Italy towards the middle of September. But until then Hal and I met fortnightly at the Baker Street flat until my departure. This brief episode was one of the happiest times in my life. It was not the most rewarding, most inspiring or most stable time but it was exhilarating because our meetings were clandestine, but without the apprehension and embarrassment of the old days at the Glaisfar hotel. I had matured and had more control within the relationship. Hal appeared to sense this. We enjoyed each other unconditionally, both knowing one day it would have to end. On my departure, we agreed I would make contact with him at his office over the following year and we made some vague plans to meet in Italy which both of us knew were highly improbable. I wanted to move on but I also wanted Hal with me. In reality, I knew we had very different interests and lifestyles and that the ten-year age gap between us was beginning to display a downside. Hal was interested in his work and work politics, house prices and football. I was into the Rolling Stones, CND (with limits) and Renaissance Italy. Then there was 'the unmentionable', Hal's family. He avoided any reference to them as much as possible but I knew they always did something together as a family on Saturdays and that he and Julia had friends to dinner or were invited elsewhere. Their bourgeois lifestyle irritated me but I envied Julia's security within her marriage. Hal felt he was doing something 'forbidden' by having a mistress and kicking against society's mores. I sort of fitted into his lifestyle together with the Jaguar, the pretty wife, the five-bedroom house with double garages, complete with gardener and daily. I sarcastically pointed out to him that I did not quite fit the bill for the added accessory, 'businessman's mistress'. The latter usually sported dyed blonde hair and false eyelashes, set off to perfection with a mini-skirt and stiletto heels. I was a bit of a scruffy, 'studenty' type. Hal responded calmly that he was a civil engineer not a businessman. He rarely responded to my jibes as he knew how emotionally hurt I still felt. He also knew that if we just met for sex without including dinner or entertainment, I would seize on that as his 'using me only for sex'. But sometimes when we went out, his exhaustion began to show. I remember the evening when we went to see the Antonioni film 'Blow Up' that was all the rage in London. I had already seen it once before with Alan and Alan had made interesting comments about the film's surrealism and intended message. Hal showed interest only in the 'three in a bed' sex scene and he found the film's direction 'slow' like many European films of the time. In fact, he fell asleep half-way through it and didn't wake up till the end. I was furious with him and we argued a lot that evening and I meted out to him the 'Wilf Jones silent treatment' during our journey back to Baker Street in a taxi. When we finally opened the door of the flat I exploded.

"Hal, I don't know what the matter with you is. Next time we will go and see Barbara Windsor and Sid James in 'Carry on Snoozing'!"

"You are totally unreasonable. Alex had toothache during the night and Julia was up and down like a yo-yo. I've had a hard day at work and I'm exhausted! God, you sound like Julia. Just for once, can you consider someone else other than yourself?"

Here it was again. Domesticity reminding me that Hal was sharing a bed with another woman, he was only on loan, briefly. Tears sprang to my eyes and he put his arms around me.

"I know it's hard darling, but this is the price we pay for being together."

I clung to him sobbing. "I love you so much. It seems so unfair."

We made up our differences in bed but I pretended to myself that I wasn't leaving for Italy and that everything would continue the same for many years to come. Whenever I hear Gerry Rafferty's soul-searching music, 'Baker Street' I always think back to those very precious moments I spent with Hal in the apartment of the street with same name.

Unbeknown to me, I suffered constant criticism from Pearl's intended, Kevin Loach. Pearl stupidly (in my view) told him about myself and Hal but spared the details of our early meeting and my termination. Kevin took it upon himself to champion the cause of Alan, girlfriend up North notwithstanding, saying that I was being unfaithful and treating Alan badly. He kept on saying that married men return to their wives.

"Oh, leave it Kevin!" Pearl said impatiently, "he hasn't **left** his wife yet so just drop it. Sian and Alan have a very casual relationship and I know she loves Hal."

"If I were Alan, I'd get this geezer knee-capped. I don't want you thinking you can carry on like 'er, Bird. One man, one woman; that's what I say."

Kevin was insistent about Pearl moving in with him and he applied so much pressure that she moved out of our flat in Maida Vale two months earlier than she should have, leaving me to fund her part of the rent. I was angry over this but could not bring myself to discuss it with her at the time. Hal helped out financially but I hated having to ask him for money as it made me feel 'a kept mistress', a sort of Mandy Rice-Davies. As I was desperately short of cash I finally did ask him. In addition to the rent money, Hal bought me a fashionable little silver choker on a velvet strip from the King's Road. I question him about how he managed to get to the King's Road from Baker Street during work time as he was always at meetings and pressed for time. I did not ask as I was touched by the appropriateness of his gift and refused to dispel the illusion that he had chosen it himself. The rational side of me assumed he had asked his secretary to choose it on his behalf.

Kevin sped around London at one hundred miles an hour. He worked with Pearl at 'Flatfinders' but had plans for opening a similar agency himself in South London. He was constantly changing his 'motor' to something bigger and more powerful and treated his reluctant audience to diatribes about 'fast motors', 'bargain motors' and 'latest motors.' Then there were 'the geezers that repaired the motors' and he recited the names of the various garages between the West End and Forest Hill like a shopping list. Kevin was definitely a candidate for Mastermind in his own speciality area. He was by no means an unpleasant person and was incredibly helpful and generous to a fault, but he could be both irritating and overpowering with his constant focus on money-making schemes which changed from week to week and varied according to whose company he happened to be in at the time. There was always something new to buy, develop, or investigate. Pearl loved his enthusiasm for life and said he was "great in bed." The only thing I could imagine about Kevin in bed was his rush to orgasm when he thought of an E-type Jaguar. I told myself to hold off the cynicism as part of me was envious of Pearl's unencumbered relationship with Kevin.

Kevin persuaded Pearl to introduce him to her parents so they visited Foistneth the following March. Kevin had spoken to Wilf and Dora a couple of times on the telephone but Pearl insisted that they kept their living together a secret as it would morally outrage both of them, particularly Wilf. Wilf was a staunch supporter of 'moral uprightness' and sexual indiscretions before and after marriage were of salacious interest but should never, ever include members of his own family. Fortunately, Dora's dalliance with the deacon remained unknown throughout his life. Wilf and Dora found Kevin charming as he raced around making business plans to extend the café. He suggested an American-style coffee bar complete with Formica surfaces and metal stools; a state-of-the-art coffee machine with 'one arm bandits' (early fruit machines) for 'the passing soldier en route to barracks' trade. He also showed innate shrewdness by never ceasing to congratulate Wilf on his business acumen. Kevin managed to include a museum for 'speciality motors' after spying Wilf's old Ford in the rickety shed known as Privy 2. Kevin even spotted an opportunity for Privy 2 but Wilf drew the line at this burst of creativity and turned down Kevin's suggestion for selling wine-making kits from the shed.

"You should marry him, our Pearl", said Dora, "he's such a lovely man. I was married with a child at your age and he'll make money, I can tell you that now."

Pearl found herself under pressure to marry from both Kevin and her parents. Anna was in America at Boston University School of Medicine studying clinical psychology and I had left for Italy. Pearl didn't have any real friends in London that could have advised her, although very like me, she showed headstrong determination in matters of the heart. It was very unlikely that she would have taken our well-meaning advice. Marriage offered her the possibility of her own home and security so when Pearl married in the June of 1968 part of her desperately wanted to believe that she would be happy with Kevin.

I was able to attend Pearl's wedding in the village in June because my teaching at the Faculty of Languages at Catania University had officially finished for the summer months. About six weeks before Pearl's wedding, I had met the man whom I believed would have a great influence on my life, the Sicilian journalist Benedetto Scalia. I was very attracted to him intellectually as well as physically and our relationship was in its early days of all-consuming passion and we had slept together a couple of times. Because of Beni, I decided not to contact Hal the week I was in England, although there were occasions when I came perilously close to telephoning his office. Anna did not attend the wedding as she was still studying in New England, USA and did not have the money for the airline ticket. She had told us in her last letter that Dr Klein was weary of funding her, particularly since the course was four years long and there were no bursaries for non-nationals. Anna worked in a hamburger bar at evenings and weekends to fund her living expenses and a reluctant Dr Klein supplemented her income.

Dora and her sister Brenda the Boast, now back on good terms with each other, made all the wedding arrangements because Pearl was living in London. A chapel wedding at the village was to be followed by the wedding breakfast in the chapel vestry. Because Kevin stated he was brought up Church of England, the planning of the religious ceremony veered between the church and the chapel in driven arguments about tradition. But Dora's deacon won the day and they finally settled for the chapel. Pearl looked lovely in her long-sleeved white dress with short billowing veil. Kevin's family, friends and relatives arrived from Forest Hill and Plumstead, Southeast London, the day before the wedding. Most stayed in 'bed and breakfast' accommodation, although some were billeted out with Brenda's family. Kevin's father and stepmother stayed with Wilf and Dora. Kevin's father was an older and wizened version of Kevin. Kevin's mother had died when he was eleven (I learned later that she had taken her own life) and he didn't care much for 'Big Lil', his stepmother, but they buried the hatchet temporarily as Kevin wanted his father - together with his brother and two sisters and their families, to attend his wedding in Wales. My mother maliciously observed that Kevin's father and his wife Lil had said the word 'bleedin' about twenty times in one minute. It was 'bleedin train' to 'bleedin vol-au-vents' to 'bleedin kids' and 'bleedin vicar'. My mother found a collective noun, 'Bleeders', to group all persons related to Kevin. She later extended this to include anyone born and bred in London with a certain accent denoting working-class origins. She commented on how 'poor' Kevin's relatives looked. She said she had seen better quality clothes on stalls at Foistneth market. Whilst standing for a congregation rendition of 'All things bright and beautiful', my mother leaned across me, the feather plumes of her hat tickling my nose, making me want to sneeze. She whispered a rumour she had heard about Kevin's sister Mary who had children in care due to 'awful abuse' by one of her ex-partners. She said Pearl had no idea what sort of family she was marrying into. I thought that was rich, coming from my mother, who had married into a similar family causing a lifetime of distress to her own parents as well as to herself. I found myself questioning whether human beings ever learned anything from their mistakes.

Pearl's wedding was emotionally moving mainly because of the Welsh singing which was musically rich and heartfelt. The male voice choir sang 'Ar Hyd Y Nos' (All Through The Night) but I could not help thinking that this particular piece of music would be more appropriate for Hal Stanton than for Kevin. The Baptist Minister chose a meaningful reading, avoiding any reference to his favourite topic, adultery. This popular Sunday topic was usually preceded by the biblical story of Samson and Delilah and how her 'feminine wiles had seduced and reduced a strong and clever man to weakness and sin.' I used to relate this story to Hal, complete with imitation of the histrionics of the Baptist Minister, the Reverend Morgan-Morgan. His voice would shake with emotion as he balefully glared at the 'adulterous' middle-aged and fashion free ladies sitting before him. He would lean over the pulpit, his Adam's apple quivering as he articulated slowly in a mellifluous voice:

"Thou shalt not commit adultery; Delilahs, they abound!"

I remembered thinking that the beautiful, biblical Delilah bore not the minimum resemblance to the stout and weather-beaten farmers' wives in the congregation. The chapel deacon would sit with bowed head saying ever so softly, "yeah, yeah. Amen." Hal would laugh till tears ran down his face, as I related the scene at the chapel but there was none of that today apart from mentioning the importance of faith within 'the sanctity of marriage'. He would have had every reason for concern had he known that Kevin had more faith in kneecapping than in religion.

Brenda was a splendid cook and expert caterer and the food was a cut above the usual Foistneth fare. Wilf had had to be persuaded to keep out of the catering arrangements but he reluctantly succumbed to his wife's entreaties as Brenda refused to have another organiser involved. All that was required of him was to pay the bill when it arrived. Wilf 'putted' disconsolately in the corner of the vestry, chatting to 'Big Lil' who true to her name and gargantuan size, gorged unashamedly on four vol-au-vents together. Dean dashed around the place in his new suit stopping fleetingly to chat with the deacon. I looked good in my expensive Italian dress with matching jacket and I sported a deep tan which suited me. Pearl said I looked beautiful. "You look a bit like Jackie Kennedy", she said, "too classy for here." I had cleaned up my student act because in Catania people were elegant, conventionally dressed and well groomed. Also, it was expected of me in my job at the University. Sicilians tended to sneer at the British lack of dress sense but all the men loved Mary Quant's miniskirt. To be fair, the cut and quality of Italian clothes were far superior to British clothes of the time but not half as much fun.

A young farmer approached me and asked me how I was. He also showed an interest in Anna saying he hoped she was not still in the Middle East as it was "a hot bed of trouble with the Arabs." I told him she was in America and he seemed relieved. I remembered him from Grammar School; he had been quite keen on Anna at the time. I walked alone down to the eight-arched bridge when Pearl and Kevin were having some additional photographs taken outside the vestry door - I couldn't fathom out why. I heard Dora shouting, "get in the next photo, Wilf. You are the father of the bride." Thank goodness she hadn't had any alcohol yet! That would follow later at the local pub where wedding guests would pay for their own drinks. Then Dora would treat us once again to tales of Lyons' Nippies, Jennifer Jones, and being approached by the serial killer Christie.

I looked across the Usk, at the relentless flow of the river with the muted hues of the Table Mountain stretching into the far distance. It reawakened nostalgic images of our shared childhoods. This was the bridge where we three children each had our own arch and named it after ourselves. Mine on the far right of the bridge, Pearl on the far left and Anna in the middle. How different our lives had panned out to the way we had planned them. Six years ago, I had stood on that very bridge wanting to kill myself over Hal Stanton. I remembered my desperation and despair and I felt strongly that I would never forgive Hal for that, not ever. But I was glad I did not die that day because we had met again and the experience had been rewarding in so many ways. I had moved on and I was now the one who had left him. My new love was at least single and free. I believed my relationship with Hal to be well and truly over. But it angered me that Hal, instead of Beni, should feature so much in my thoughts. Part of me knew that I was only fooling myself if I believed I had totally erased Harold Stanton from my mind.

Chapter 12

Music: *'Layla'*. Eric Clapton, (1970)

My work at the University of Catania began well. It mostly involved teaching English to undergraduate students and helping the Professor of Faculty with her research into the English Romantic poets. Catania is a large commercial town in eastern Sicily, on the Ionian seacoast and south of Mount Etna, an active volcano. It had a mild climate but there were brief cold winters and frustratingly long, blazing summers. The city stifled in the summer and there were frequent water shortages. Many of the affluent middle-classes had summer villas on the coast or in the hills towards Mount Etna where there were no water shortages. Neither were there water shortages at the private 'lidi' where it was common for families to hire a wood beach cabin for three months. These beach enterprises made a considerable amount of money in the summer season as they not only rented out cabins for changing into swimwear at exorbitantly high prices but had takings from the bar selling every conceivable kind of hot and cold snacks as well as ice-cream, cold drinks and alcoholic beverages. There were plenty of showers for the guests and lack of fresh water for commercial use was never an issue at any lido. The water shortages were in the most socially deprived areas of the city, with the highest density of population.

I shared a large apartment with an English girl called Jeanette who taught at a private college and a university lecturer from Northern Italy called Maria-Pia. I preferred Maria-Pia to Jeanette who had lived in Catania three years and believed she knew more about Italy than the Italians. She spoke Italian with the most grating English accent that I mimicked constantly to my friends and acquaintances. But in the early months, before I met Beni, I was glad of her and her boyfriend's company. I met Beni for the first time through a mutual friend at the university. We went on a trip to the Greek amphitheatre at Syracuse, followed by lunch at a local rustic restaurant. Beni was a very knowledgeable and interesting man. He was also good-looking. He was average height for a man, about the same height as Hal but thin and angular with unruly brown hair sweeping low across his forehead above his brooding dark eyes. He was constantly restless and gave the impression of being impulsively agitated by some inner torment. He smoked incessantly. But he was sharp, extremely well read and an excellent conversationalist. When we became lovers after a couple of dates, he told me a little about his work. He worked for a national newspaper as the local correspondent for Calabria and Sicily. His main office was based in Palermo but he worked from a smaller one in Catania. His family were from Catania but he had moved out of home and rented his own apartment the year before we met as he felt his mother was meddling too much in his love life and he needed freedom of manoeuvre. His sister Carmela was two years younger and she lived at home with her parents. Beni told me that he hated what mafia corruption had done to the luscious and historic island of Sicily and said he would support anyone who would challenge the mafia, whether an ordinary individual, a politician or an institution. That is why he had become a journalist, to expose corruption in all quarters where he could. He was adamant that political corruption existed and reached into the judiciary, the various branches of police force and even the Vatican itself. He was angry that some of his articles were either editorially sanitised or lay unpublished because his editor in Palermo had been 'leaned on' and would pay a high price if he offended anyone of importance and social standing involved in corruption. Any individual standing up to the mafia was eventually murdered or forced into submission by threat and he said he knew it would happen to him some day. I tended to find this a little over dramatic but as time went on I had more and more reason to believe it. There was evidence of corruption as I witnessed written but unsigned threats to Beni's life.

Beni and I went to England together the year after Pearl's wedding. This time we went to London for the christening of her son Dylan. I was chosen to be godmother to the baby but little did I know at the time that Pearl had difficulty convincing Kevin that I had the sort of 'moral values' to ensure the child would have a Christian upbringing. He kept saying to Pearl: "what about that married geezer she was with? Now she's with this Ai Tie geezer! What sort of moral example is that for Dylan?" But our friendship was so deep that Pearl overruled him, a most uncommon occurrence for Pearl these days. I thought Dylan absolutely beautiful. He didn't look much like either Pearl or Kevin but was a genetic blend of the two. Wilf and Dora were the proud grandparents, although Dora didn't hold Dylan for long as she needed to light a cigarette and Pearl would not allow her to puff smoke over the baby.

Anna was back in England after leaving the USA five weeks before. She had graduated and was looking for clinical psychology experience in England before returning to Israel to work and live with Yossi. He would be coming to London himself this year and Anna wanted to introduce him to her parents. But the Kleins were not keen on Anna marrying an Israeli, mainly because they would lose her to Israel. Juliet also intimated that Anna should consider the possibility that Yossi might be marrying her to get a visa for the UK as "it is not uncommon for Israelis to use British Jews in their own interest". This kind of talk made Anna angry and although her mother's arguments were not totally without foundation, it was untrue in this case. Yossi already had a work visa for the USA as he was born there. He was a professional person, an archaeologist, and had chosen to live in Israel. Anna felt she and Juliet would never establish a mother and daughter relationship so long as her mother continued to criticise and undermine any idea she had or any plan she ever made. From time to time, I used to look at the photograph of Anna at the christening, clutching Dylan very close to her with the christening font in the background complete with stone crucifix. She was wearing a very large, gold Star of David around her neck. The picture looked bizarre and begged some sort of satirical caption such as: 'Jewish mother confuses baby'. We all laughed when the picture was developed, apart from Kevin, who couldn't see the joke. Anna looked terrific in her fashionable modern clothes. She wore her long hair twisted into a knot on top of her head with long strands softly falling each side of her face. She was tanned and healthy-looking, her previous gawky figure and paleness subsumed into her teenage development and no longer visible. She was staying with her North London relatives whilst Beni and I stayed in a B&B in Gower Street, near my old university. Although Kevin kept repeating that they would be moving to a bigger property in Croydon shortly, Pearl and family were still in the one-bedroom flat in Forest Hill and it was very cramped. Pearl offered us accommodation but I knew Beni would be uncomfortable there. Beni's English was of a high standard but it did not extend to Cockney rhyming slang and 'geezers and motors'. I grew weary when Beni kept asking me what Kevin had said for the umpteenth time and I had to translate into Italian statements like: 'Eah, ah bet yah you doan 'ave nofink like this in It'ly guv.' But in spite of the difficulties, we three managed to get together one afternoon in a coffee bar in Carnaby Street. Kevin looked after Dylan and Beni went shopping in the West End, looking for gifts for his family My friends thought Beni very courteous and extremely attractive and both asked whether we intended getting married. I said it was too soon to consider that for various reasons. They pressed me and I listed the obstacles. First, there was the religion. Beni was Roman Catholic in name if not by practice, but I was not. This meant we would need a special dispensation from the Vatican costing a considerable amount of money if we wished to get married in church or I would have to convert to Catholicism. The easiest solution would be to marry in a registry office in England but that would upset Beni's family. Any marriage commitment would mean that I would be forced to live in Sicily - possibly for the rest of my life - as that is where Beni's career was. Last but not least, there was open antagonism from Beni's mother, who was against our relationship.

Beni's mother had begrudgingly accepted the relationship initially and had even invited me to lunch a couple of times but as time went on and I showed no signs of disappearing she grew angry and vindictive. In her opinion English girls were all 'sluts' as they slept with men before they were married. Much of Sicily thought the same way at the time, although that kind of mentality was pervasive among the less educated section of the population and mainly prevalent among individuals disinclined to outside influences. The local beauty spot and tourist attraction within an easy driving distance form Catania was a town high above sea level called Taormina. It was renowned in the 1960s and 1970s for its beautiful Swedish girls, many Britt Ekland look-alikes. But unlike Britt, who snared a famous movie star, the Swedish beauties were less discerning and had a reputation for 'sleeping with waiters and barmen' and in so doing, caused distress to local girls whose intended they were. The foreign girls' openness, lack of hypocrisy and unencumbered sexual freedom outraged the moral hygiene of the local inhabitants. Because English girls like myself travelled around and did not live with our families, we were seen as 'dangerous to Sicilian sons' and morally defective. Girls should be virgins before marriage but boys were not encouraged to follow the same norms. Beni's mother tried everything she could to get him to leave me and when she failed she went on the attack. She made abusive phone calls to me or called our apartment (in later years when we lived together) and hung up when I answered. She wrote slanderous letters to the university about me in the hope of getting me fired. Once she wrote 'BORDELLO' (brothel) in red crayon on the door of my shared apartment in Catania. Maria-Pia and Jeanette's Sicilian fiancé were outraged by this slur on their honour and went to the police to affect a prosecution for defamation. At least it curtailed the vengeance of Beni's mother for a while. Few jealous wives could have rivalled Beni's mother in the venting of hatred and wrath but neither Beni nor his long-suffering father and sister were able to do anything about it. Carmela avoided me in case her mother found out, but if we inadvertently met in the street and she was alone, she always greeted me courteously and stopped for a chat.

Anna was looking for shared accommodation in London and she said she would let me know when she had found something in case I decided to return to the UK. I did not want to do this yet as I most wanted to be with Beni in Catania but I felt it may eventually come to that. Beni was inherently neurotic and would fly off the handle at the slightest little thing. I found his volatile behaviour very difficult to handle at times.

"Mamma Mia Shanna" - he was never able to pronounce my name property – "is it possible you cannot remember to bring table napkins for the picnic? How can we hold the food in our hands now? We will sit here and starve with the food in front of us in the basket. We will die of hunger because YOU have forgotten the table napkins!" He would then whip out a cigarette and draw on it heavily with his eyes smouldering. Nothing would console him or distract him until we had driven around countless villages near Etna over a lunchtime - when most were closed - in order to find paper table napkins. It occurred to me on one occasion when Beni was having one of his tantrums that I had never seen Hal really angry. Beni got angry all the time for seemingly trivial matters although he dealt with serious issues with reflection and gravitas. He was sometimes withdrawn and morose; during these times I learned to leave him alone as I was unsure whether his silences were due to some incident related to work or to his mother. If he didn't want to talk he would move his hand dismissively. Other times he would say:

"Things are not good here, Shanna. Many people are being bought with the money intended for the regeneration of the South. The Democrazia Cristiana is the majority party of the mafia."

Political corruption greatly concerned and angered Beni but there were so many ambiguities within his character. Anger against corrupt politicians could run parallel with his anger over the missing table napkins or my lack of judgement in practical arrangements. For example, an exploitative businessman would merit the same release of pent-up frustration as I would get by bringing the wrong beach umbrella to the lido. But I knew he loved me and I believe I loved him.

I was twenty-five years old in In 1971 and I returned to England briefly for two reasons. I needed a gynaecological investigation because I was suffering with heavy abdominal pain. I had this carried out in London as Anna was now working there doing a placement in clinical psychology to convert her American qualification to a British one. Beni was busy so I went alone. I was relieved as it meant finding accommodation would be easier without him. Beni had met my mother and Theodore; both were superficially courteous but Beni immediately saw through them, labelling my mother as childish and disorganised and Theo as very repressed with appalling manners. Theodore and Mattie Boyce had parted for good and he had moved back into Davy Cottage the year after my grandmother's death for - what I considered to be - practical reasons. He needed to guard his estate in case Cliff Bayley showed up 'to steal my legacy for gambling'. Ironically, Theodore and my mother now got along much better and she did the gardening whilst he did the shopping and cooking. I thought how circumstances had so conspired to make this division of labour happen. Perhaps if they had reached this compromise long ago, our lives would have been less sad and turbulent throughout the bleak years of the 1950s and 60s.

I was given an endoscopy and in addition to heavy scar tissue around the womb, the consultant gynaecologist discovered that I had two blocked fallopian tubes which meant it was highly unlikely I would ever become pregnant. They suggested surgery should the need arise. I stayed in the Royal Free Hospital in Hampstead for two nights and on discharge went to stay with Anna at her shared accommodation in Kensal Rise. On one of the days, I went to visit Pearl in Forest Hill. She now had an addition to the family, a little daughter called Jennie who bore an uncanny likeness to Dora. The flat was even more cramped than usual with nappies everywhere and Pearl looked harassed and considerably older than I last remembered her. Kevin was still talking about buying a bigger property in Croydon. He continued to run 'a big motor'. Pearl was unable to work because of the children and also because (she said) Kevin didn't believe in wives working. The main problem was that Kevin kept changing his job - he had had four over the past year - and although a hard worker when in a job, there were nevertheless weeks without any money coming in between one job and the next. Since his employment at Flatfinders some years ago, Kevin had worked as a used car salesman, a maintenance man for C&A, a shipping clerk and even took a stall at Plumstead market with his brother where they sold white fish to the public. This involved him getting up at 3 a.m. and going to Billingsgate to buy the fish and then onto Plumstead to sell it. He was exhausted by 8 p.m. so Pearl removed her dining-room furniture and made the dining-room into the second bedroom for herself and the children so as not to disturb Kevin in the night. She rarely saw Kevin these days. She burst into tears when she told me how her marriage was getting on top of her and she had never felt so insecure and alone. Dylan fell over on the uneven garden surface and screamed for his mother to comfort him. I picked him up and handed him to her with tears streaming down his face.

"We need to get out of here Sian, but we don't have any money. Kevin does his best but he's always chopping and changing his job and I know we are behind with our mortgage payments on this flat. I dread to think what would happen if we lost our home."

"Do you want to stay with him Pearl?"

"I don't have any choice do I, with two small children? I can't go home to Foistneth. Mum and Dad have been kind but my mother and I don't hit it off for long and she keeps telling me what to feed my own children. It's annoying considering how she used to feed me and Dean on Palethorpes Pork Pies and burnt chips!"

"And don't forget the stinkerbum butter and the sherbet lemons matted with cats fur!" I ventured.

Laughter was a temporary release from the repetitive drudgery of the situation and we fell about with loud guffaws, causing Dylan to freeze and stare at us, desperately trying to fathom the scenario before him. He immediately stopped wailing, distracted by his mother's unusual behaviour. Pearl she did not laugh much these days. I left Pearl £20 and told her to hide it and spend it on the children. She could tell Kevin it was Jennie's christening gift. I must admit that when I caught the train from Forest Hill station that day I felt worried for Pearl. This was not the future she intended when she left Foistneth. I thought of Beni and his favourite Italian saying: "The whole world is nothing more than one continent, one country, one village, one family", implying that little changes in human relationships wherever you go in the world.

I contacted Hal. I don't know why I did, but impulsively I did. Part of the explanation may have been that Beni and I were going through a sticky patch and we had talked about breaking up. A horrendous row between us spiralled after our visit to the Teatro Massimo Bellini in Catania to see to 'La Traviata'. As we walked down the grand staircase on our exit from the upper circle of the theatre we met Beni's parents head on at the bottom of the stairs. There was no escape. His mother looked at me contemptuously and said aloud enough for some opera goers in the vicinity to hear:

"Well, this is a fitting opera to bring you to. For a whore and about a whore." I did not reply but as I rushed across the red carpeted floor refusing to look either side of me until I reached the exit door, tears flooded into my eyes. Then I heard a man's raised voice state contemptuously to Beni's mother: "Signora, this is an opera house, not a fish market!" I felt totally humiliated by the incident and very unsupported by Beni. He told me he had reprimanded his mother but I responded furiously saying we must either make a permanent commitment or end it as her attitude would never change towards me. Beni was ambiguous on both fronts and this made me both exasperated, bewildered and disappointed in him.

Part of me hoped I would not find Hal but I left a message at his office and he called me back the same day. He sounded genuinely pleased to hear from me and we tried to arrange a meeting. This was complicated by the fact that I was leaving in three days' time and he did not have access to the Baker Street flat anymore. We finally agreed to meet at Heathrow Airport, the evening before my departure. Hal asked me, rather tentatively, if I thought if it was okay to book a room at one of the hotels near the airport. I could leave from there the following morning. Hal certainly knew how to plan clandestine encounters but instead of angering me to jealousy as it had in the past, I found it quite amusing. I took my leave of Anna telling her my plans. She said I was crazy and could not believe that Hal Stanton was still around after eight years. She looked at me calmly as she said, "I have a feeling that this affair is not going to end well. Be careful, Sian." Echoes of my grandmother's voice ominously returned: "Think, Sian, think before you act. You are so impulsive."

I arrived at the airport and waited for Hal. When he arrived, he walked right past without recognising me. I called his name and when he looked at me, I could see his amazement. "Sian", he said, "you look so different". I did. I was slimmer and very tanned. My wavy hair was a fashionable shoulder length style and my well-cut clothes and shoes were high quality Italian. My eyes were made up in the style of Nefertiti. Hal was thrown off guard temporarily but he quickly regained confidence and he appeared proud to be seen walking around with me. He looked older and a bit thinner than when I had seen him last. He also looked very pale after Sicilian skins although in the sun Hal tanned easily as I remembered in the days of the Glaisfar. We checked into the double room at the hotel and I sorted out my clothes for the next day (Beni training) whilst Hal ordered us a drink from the bar. I sat on one of the armchairs puffing on my cigarette whilst Hal watched me, lost for words. I knew he wasn't quite sure how to play this one and what the real purpose of our meeting was. He approached it by asking me if there was anyone significant in my life. I said there was. He asked me if I loved that person; I said I did. He then asked me why I was here with him. I said I didn't know. This scenario sounded eerily familiar from another time and another place: Hal and myself in our early days of passion when I had asked him about his wife. I stubbed out my cigarette and got up slowly, making towards the bathroom. He stood up as well and he grabbed my arm suddenly.

"Is this pay-back time Sian, or do you seriously want to be here with me?" His eyes scanned my face, searching for clues. He looked perplexed but sincere.

"I really want to be here Hal, I… "

His mouth covered mine and then little by little we edged towards the bed.

We did not go down to dinner but had room service brought up. We made love three times that evening. I wanted not to enjoy it. I wanted to feel that it was a mistake and that I loved Beni but it did exactly the opposite. It convinced me how good Hal and I were together in bed and how much I really loved him. As only fate will prescribe, one of the chief executives of Hal's company had offered him a free week for himself and his family at a luxurious villa in Sardinia. The villa belonged to a Lord Tressington. Julia was not keen to go as she felt the children were not quite old enough for Italy in the scorching heat of early August, barely five weeks away. Hal said he may be able to get the villa on some pretext of work whilst telling Julia he had to go to Rome on business. But he feared she might want to accompany him if her parents could be persuaded to have the children. But on second thoughts he said that was unlikely as her mother hadn't been too well recently. If we planned it carefully and all things permitting, we could meet in Sardinia and have a whole week together.

"Sardinia's very expensive and it's quite a way to travel to spend a week in the bedroom, Hal. Wouldn't we be better off going to Margate or somewhere like that?" I said teasingly. I also had the problem of explaining my absence to Beni, who was naturally suspicious and more difficult to convince of fidelity than Julia. A half-formed plan made me believe that if I told him that I had to return to England for further gynaecological investigations, I might just get away with it. But I would need to enlist Anna's help as Beni was likely to telephone the flat. I'd have to work at finalising the sharper details but it sounded good in theory. I would book my return ticket to England from Catania but as the plane stopped in Rome anyway I would then switch planes and purchase a ticket to Sardinia, on the same day. Hal would meet me in Rome and we'd travel to Sardinia together. We parted feeling greatly enthusiastic with our plans of deception. I was to contact him to ensure there were no drastic changes to the plan and to update myself on the arrangement details. As I waved to him from the steps of the aircraft, I realised that I had never felt so loved and content in my whole life.

My feelings of inner contentment were short-lived. Beni was waiting for me at Catania airport suggesting with some enthusiasm that we drove to a trattoria in the hills for lunch. The restaurant was famous for its fresh ricotta made on site and its mushroom and cream pasta dishes. "Do you have the afternoon off?" I asked him, surprised. "Yes", he said. "I wanted to take you out because I need to talk to you". He seemed calm and contained which made me both curious and concerned. Such a statement from him with my current guilty conscience would seriously be cause for alarm. After the main course, Beni reached across the table and took my hand. The restaurant was high above sea level and the blue vista of the Ionian Sea stretched ahead of us and far into the distance. This stunning panorama overlooking fishing villages along the Northern Coastline is one of the most beautiful I have ever seen. White rivulets on the dark blue sea showed signs of breakers, or perhaps waves disturbed by the buzzing activity of motorboats that haunted these waters in summer. White villas with sloping terracotta roofs adorned the shoreline, and above all this rises the steep grandeur of Mount Etna, overseeing the landscape and ostentatiously contributing to its diversity with breath-taking elegance and beauty. The volcano was non-active at present but it could change at any time and begin to regurgitate a boiling lava fountain of red flames hundreds of feet into the air. Sometimes in early summer Etna's highest tip and immediate surrounds were overlaid with dazzling snow whilst people from towns and villages scattered among the hills below sunbathed on the beaches along the shore.

On impulse, Beni pulled a small, gift-wrapped box out of his pocket and offered it to me. "Open it Shanna."

It was an exquisite ruby and diamond ring. He smiled as I looked at it in wonderment.

"Will you consider marrying me, Shanna? You know I love you".

Tears surged to my eyes. Oh, why now? Why this timing? Why not before my trip to England? I would not have contacted Hal if only I had known his intention.

"Dearest Beni I can't. I can't marry you..."

"Why not? Are you married already?"

"Of course not. I... I don't think I will be able to have children, Beni, I've just learned something about myself and we can't make this decision lightly. Dearest, thank you for asking me but there are so many things... including your mother.."

"My mother again! Let's leave her out of it. I am not a child anymore. I make my own decisions; if she doesn't like it then I'm sorry. He shrugged his shoulders. Forget my mother Shanna".

"She won't let me forget her. Beni, seriously, I have to return to England in a few weeks for more gynaecological investigations..."

"I will come with you."

"It's not necessary, Beni - it shouldn't be more than a few days. You need to know whether we can have children because you will regret your decision to marry me for the rest of your life, especially as there is so much opposition from your family."

Not even Hal Stanton could have carried out such barefaced lies and deceit with such aplomb. As Beni and I made love at our flat that afternoon, I remembered my morning of passion with Hal in the hotel at Heathrow Airport not many hours before. Mattie Boyce suddenly came to mind. I had to agree with Beni's mother, I felt and acted no better than a whore.

Chapter 13

Music: *'Killing Me Softly'*, Roberta Flack (1973)

We took a taxi from Olbia airport to Lord Tressington's villa called 'Lion Rock' which was about twenty kilometres away. We had been advised to take a taxi as there were only unmarked tracks, frequently without asphalt, leading to the discreetly tucked away luxury villas along the coastline. This was a very different island to Sicily. Sicily had stark contrasts of landscape; industrialisation sat comfortably in contrast with a rich cultural heritage and monuments belonging to the ancient past. Northern Sardinia was one big landscape of emerald sea, luxury hotels, flawless beaches and marinas for the yachts of the rich.

The taxi-driver had a problem finding the villa which we had predicted he would. Hal was hot and irritable as he had been travelling since the morning, unlike my fifty-minute flight from Catania to Rome followed by a thirty-minute ride to Olbia. Hal was anxious "to phone Julia before she decides to phone me." He had given her the number of the villa and this enraged me.

"What if she rings? She thinks you are in Rome so what if the telephone operator informs her that the code she has is Sardinia not Rome? What if I pick the phone up? You are sailing very close to the wind, Hal."

"Sian, for heaven's sake! Why don't you worry about the Italian fellow and leave me to worry about my wife?"

I sat in silence then, very cross with him. Here we were together on our first holiday, on one of the most beautiful islands in the world, and we were bickering like an old married couple. Finally, we got to the villa. It was expensively furnished in the best possible taste. An interior designer had obviously been at work here. It had eight bedrooms, each with its own name according to décor: 'violet room', 'green room' etc. The maid had made up the 'royal blue' room and we had a most magnificent view of the lion rock itself in the centre of the private beach. It was called 'lion rock' because of a gigantic rock mass that sat proudly in an otherwise unblemished sweep of pale white sand leading to the shoreline and beyond to the emerald sea. From a distance and at certain angles, the rock mass looked like the erect head of a lion, complete with flowing mane.

There was a yacht at anchor in the shimmering bay. Hal grabbed his binoculars and said the yacht was 'The Cristina' and it belonged to the Greek billionaire Aristotle Onassis. We eventually showered and unpacked, discovering the kitchen which had two gigantic freezers full of food. Whilst I rustled around in the fridges looking for something not too complicated to cook for dinner, Hal attempted to ring Julia from the house telephone. When he finally got through he kept his voice so low that I could not hear what he was saying. I felt angry that Julia had intruded on us even here. But sex soon distracted us and then I remembered it was eleven o'clock and I had forgotten to ring Beni. I got through to Catania without too much difficulty but there was no reply. Beni was out. I heaved a sigh of relief but when I got back to the Blue Room, Hal was already fast asleep so I climbed into bed and put my arms around him, my face nestling against his back. In spite of some minor setbacks, I experienced contentment that evening.

We spent a happy week at Lion Rock but we saw precious little of Sardinia. We visited Porto Cervo on the Costa Smeralda once and we walked around the marina, looking at the boats and browsing in the expensive shops selling luxury goods and envying the social ease of the expensively attired customers. The marina was full of opulent boats with liveried servants belonging to the world's wealthiest businessmen, celebrities and minor royalty. We both sported dark suntans and Hal looked ten years younger than when we had arrived. Bizarrely as it might appear, given the nature of our relationship over eight years, I knew very little about Hal's past life. In Sardinia I got to know him more as a person. Hal's job required a lot of precision work with mathematical calculation. It somehow did not fit with this person taking dangerous personal risks with his marriage by telling his wife he was at a hotel in Rome, hoping she would not ring the number or discover the STD code was not Rome at all. He said he needed access to his family in case one of the children was suddenly taken ill. If the phone rang, I would answer it with a business-like 'pronto' in case Julia Stanton was on the other end. I rang Anna and told her to tell Beni if he contacted that I had gone to Wales to visit my mother. The telephone exchange where my mother lived was so difficult to pronounce and the line so bad that I was sure Beni would give up on it. I rang him twice during the week saying I was okay, missing him and would be back at the weekend. Hal and I hired a car for three days so as to visit some places of interest on the island. I drove most of the time as I was familiar with driving on the right and had passed my driving test in Catania. I now spoke conversational Italian fluently.

Hal and I made love constantly, in different parts of the house, on the beach and in the motorboat. One scorching afternoon we went out in the boat and we lay naked on our towels on the top of it, drifting in the bay with the engine of the boat switched off. Hal was reading but I didn't have the energy to even do that. Suddenly our eyes met and I looked deep into the dark irises of Hal's blue eyes. Our glance held and we both knew what the other wanted. He made as if to reach for me and I was aware of the size of his erection. I held up my hand. "Hal", I said "do you think we could reach orgasm without touching each other?"

I explained that if we lay next to each other concentrating on each other's bodies and thinking about sex we should mentally get to orgasm. I suggested that whichever one of us was about to come should slide onto the floor of the boat waiting for the other to position themselves on top, leading the other in joint orgasm. There was something very wild and abandoning about this in the middle of the sea with the occasional hum of the motorboats as they flashed by. Many of the coves were private so there were few people around even in August when this particular coast had its highest number of well-heeled summer visitors. We attempted my plan. It took us less than five minutes to approach mental orgasm with eyes fixed on each other's bodies. He moved to the floor of the boat first and I slid after him my body shaking with pleasure as I tried to hold back until he penetrated me. I came on top of him and as I moved my body downward onto his penis he gave a yell of unrestricted, pure abandonment. I joined him screaming with pleasure as I reached orgasm. We lay panting like animals on the floor of the boat, our bodies awash with the liquid aftermath of sex. With our sexual appetites temporarily slaked, we lay there for a few minutes kissing each other tenderly and lovingly in the heat of the sun as the boat drifted gently towards Lion Rock.

The evening before our departure from Sardinia, we found ourselves invited to a neighbour's house for a light buffet, drinks and conversation. There were about fifteen people present at the gathering but only one or two native English speakers. All the others were Italian or German with Italian being the predominant language of social interaction. I found myself able to converse with all present but Hal was more or less restricted to the English-speaking people. I did not tell them that I worked in Catania but said Hal and I lived together in London. Because they commented that my Italian had a Southern intonation, I told them that I had worked for three years at Catania University. Being from the North, the guests held the South in scant regard and made some derogatory remarks I knew would have infuriated Beni. Mainly out of laziness, but also with some hesitation due to respect for my hosts, I decided not to champion the Southern Italian cause with counter arguments to their foundation-less and ill-informed comments.

Hal and I drove home and on our arrival at the villa I suggested our usual nightcap before we went to bed. "No", Hal said, "I've had enough to drink and you certainly have."

"What do you mean?" I said annoyed. "I haven't had that much. What's got into you?"

"If you wish to flirt with other men Sian, that is your choice but at least show me the courtesy not to carry on in front of me."

"Who or what are you referring to in particular?"

"To the airline pilot who asked for your telephone number. I may have no knowledge of Italian but I am not stupid."

At this precise moment he reminded me of Beni who had the annoying habit of prefacing his remarks with, "I may not teach at a university, but I am not stupid!". It is true I had given the pilot my London number on request, but I doubted he would ever call me there. Hal was right, I probably was a little too tipsy and the pilot had taken advantage of this by asking for my number. What I had never witnessed before was any possessiveness from Hal. I had always been the possessive one and I was suddenly touched by this turn of events. Hal stood gazing across at the moonlit bay overlooked by the wide patio windows of our main living room. He was wearing an elegant black shirt and he hugged his arms across his chest as he stood staring across the water, his face unsmiling and stern.

"Onassis has gone from the bay", he said detachedly.

"Hal, darling. I am so sorry that I offended you. Believe me, it was not intentional and not at all as you perceive it to be. Maybe I did have too much to drink. I talk too much when I do and I shouldn't have left you on your own with those boring people..."

He continued to look out across the bay in silence. I felt helpless and then I approached him slowly and lightly kissed him on the forehead.

"Don't let's spoil our last evening with this trivial argument, darling. Please. We don't know when we are going to see each other again. I didn't dare voice my innermost thoughts, 'perhaps never'.

He looked away from the bay and dragged his eyes towards mine.

He said softly, "I love you Sian. I feel we need to be together."

Hal had said the words I had so desperately wanted for him to say, needed to hear him say, for seven or eight long years. I had only ever heard his words in my dreams and had woken up feeling a sense of perfect peace and wanting to stay asleep with my dream forever. Never, even in the throes of our wildest and abandoned love making had Hal told me he loved me.

I reached out towards him, my voice trembling with emotion, "Oh I love you so much darling, but you have always known that".

"Yes, he said, responding to my touch but without the usual passionate physical response, "I know. But Sian, we have consequences to face."

We stayed awake until the early hours planning our future. He said he would leave Julia. Their marriage had been rocky for some years but the last eighteen months had been hell. She would take him to the cleaners financially, especially if she knew another woman was involved, so their separation had to be done gradually, slowly over the coming months. But there would be an upper time limit of a year. I needed to work the three months' notice required by Catania University. I probably would be able to leave Sicily at Christmas and in the meantime apply for work in London. I would also need to find accommodation but I assumed I could stay with Anna in the interim.

And Beni? I didn't even want to think about him but I knew I would eventually tell him that I needed to end our relationship. It wasn't as if we had not discussed it enough in the past but the thought of abruptly ending our relationship in this traumatic and deceitful manner left a bitter taste in my mouth. I repeated that it would be so much better for him and of course, so much better for his mother but my self-justifications felt hollow. We finally fell asleep without making love, for once.

It was a bit of a rush getting off in the morning to catch the 11 a.m. plane to Rome. We bundled our cases into the hire car with Hal doing the last-minute checks to see if we had forgotten anything. In spite of his lack of experience in laundry and culinary matters, he was more practical and organised than I was. This time he drove along the dirt track where the villa was situated leading to the main 'A' road leading to Olbia airport. He drove at speed suddenly swerving to the left and pulling off the road. The car bounced as he drove over the rough terrain in the direction of the sea. " Hal, what are you doing?" I was temporarily stunned by his actions and began to forcefully protest. He turned off the car engine suddenly and turned towards me. "I want us to say goodbye here, facing the sea". He gently removed my sunglasses and placed them gently on the dashboard. He leaned forward and kissed me, his tongue avidly searching my mouth for mine. In a moment of passion, I unzipped him and he pulled my mouth down on his penis. We were both oblivious to the possibility that a motorist could arrive any minute and we would be arrested for indecent behaviour. Hal told me to get out of the car. I did in a daze. He then slid across onto the passenger seat. "Sit on me Sian", he said breathlessly; "ease yourself gently onto my cock". He eased down my scanty briefs and I lowered myself onto his erect penis. As he moved up and down inside me with his hand pressing against my stomach he said, "look at the view and the emerald sea. Look at this spectacle and never forget what we were doing here this last day in Sardinia". Absurdly a vision popped into my mind of Humphrey Bogart saying to Ingrid Bergman in Casablanca, "we'll always have Paris." I wondered whether they had attempted anything like this on the Champs-Elysees. Although concerned about being discovered by a curious onlooker, I gasped in panting compliance and abandoned myself to orgasm. He joined me within half a second of my coming and we groaned and moved together making the car shake and roll from side to side.

We got to Olbia airport with less than ten minutes to spare before the closure of the check-in.

Chapter 14

Music: *'Anonimo Veneziano'* (1970) Stelvio Cipriani

After spending a week in the sun my skin had turned as dark as an average Sicilian's. I was tanned before I left Sicily but I feared Beni might question why I came back from England the colour of a Nigerian and had hastily prepared a story about visits to a solarium in London. I was telling so many lies that I was meeting myself coming backwards and I was petrified of being caught out and the consequences it would bring. In reality, if I was exposed it mattered less now than it had before but the last thing I wanted was to hurt Beni. But Beni appeared distracted by his own thoughts, telling me he needed to spend a week at his head office in Palermo. His mind was undoubtedly on other matters and I vaguely wondered whether his mother had been causing trouble again in my absence. Beni told me briefly that there would be an imminent court hearing featuring a known mafioso, quite high up in the criminal fraternity. A judge from the North of Italy was to try the case in Palermo as local judges were vulnerable to corruption. Their families would be threatened if they refused to co-operate. Beni once told me how a local judge, selected to sit at a criminal trial of a local mafioso, received a stolen photograph of his sixteen-year-old daughter. The photograph contained slashes to across the girl's face made painstakingly by a razor blade. On the back of the photograph was scrawled: "next time it will not be the photograph." Needless to say, the judge capitulated. I admitted to Beni that I could never understand the Sicilian mentality and why people did not unite and try to defend themselves against corruption. Beni said:

"Sian, it is not so easy. You need to understand the people of the South. The mafia were hired originally to protect the common people from cruel and corrupt landowners. Instead, the very people hired to protect them became even more corrupt than the landowners. The mentality of fear, protection and corruption is pervasive here. If your loved ones were threatened, what choice would you have, what would **you** do?"

Beni and I would argue for hours about this and I made suggestions as to what I believed I would and could do given a particular set of circumstances. I always believed that people had choices and if they did not then they should fight together to change things but I was proved wrong in the goodness of time.

I carried on with my bits of summer work for the university, preparing course materials and re-sit examinations for September. Catania was scorching in August and we were too far from the sea to benefit from the occasional evening breeze. Our flat was in a built-up area of the town with buildings that stubbornly clung to heat of the day and through the night. Sometimes I slept on the tiles of the bathroom floor in my desperate attempt to find some temporary relief from the airless warmth. I visualised Hal and myself making love in different positions, like the time we did it in front of the mirror at the villa, observing our every movement, with Hal providing a sensual commentary. Then our 'mental orgasm' on the motorboat and the sheer bliss of our last morning in Sardinia. Hal was a very sensuous man and our love making had never been so intense or so satisfying. This is not how it was in Baker Street where he had to encourage me to overcome my shyness and gently coerce me to make love totally naked with the light on. I had always felt sexually inhibited, until now. Hal taught me to enjoy my body without shame, and he had a way of holding me and caressing me that drove me to a state of pure sexual frenzy. Our relationship at times had veered dangerously close to eroticism rather than love. My vagina felt sore from his frequent and prolonged penetrations. Hal was phenomenal at holding off orgasm until I was ready to come. No other man I had slept with was able to do that with such consideration for my pleasure and with so much expertise. But I wondered sometimes whether living together would dull our passion for one another or restrict our relationship to little beyond erotica and sexual gratification.

I was glad that Beni's libido was diminished and his thoughts preoccupied elsewhere. About the middle of September, Beni told me that he had to go to Palermo to cover a trial of a corrupt real estate developer. The individual concerned had made substantial land purchases to sell on to the government for social housing. Certain landowners were forced to sell to the developer at rock bottom prices on pain of 'inconvenience to their family.' It was an offer they could not refuse. The deception was that the cheap land was then sold on to the government for a hefty asking price. It was of poor quality and situated in areas so lacking in infrastructure that some of the cesspits were not joined to the main sewers. Water was only available a few times a week for four long months in the summer because it was diverted to the fruit farms and the money-generating beach enterprises along the Sicilian coastline. These people paid the local mafia handsomely for the privilege of having no water shortages during the summer months. The poor could not afford to do so and their interests were of small account. The final outcome was that the developer charged the Regional Government top prices for the land and false information was provided regarding its market value and completed infrastructure. The developer then used the government's money to purchase prime plots of land close to the sea for the construction of luxury homes. He built high-rise shanty towns for the poor in the inland areas. Some of these high-rise buildings had collapsed following a minor earth tremor two years ago prior. People died under the rubble or suffered life-long injuries. Sicily was prone to earth tremors of different degrees of intensity and buildings were constructed with this knowledge in mind but over three hundred people died as a consequence of the collapsed buildings in the region of Palermo including small children. The government finally took action and the developer was indicted for corruption and manslaughter but he blamed others and maintained his innocence. Beni was reporting on the case and he had interviewed many witnesses anonymously, as they were too frightened to speak out publicly. Unbeknown to me, Beni was also taking a great personal risk to his own life.

There are often flash storms with torrential rain in Catania in early September. As the town drainage facilities were inadequate, the street sewers became quickly blocked and the overflowing water seeped upwards into the streets causing havoc for pedestrians and vehicles. People were often forced to abandon their cars on pavements and make a run for it. On such a day in mid-September I crossed the road to our apartment dripping wet, trying to dodge the rainwater pouring from the gutters and reaching almost to my knees. As I fumbled for the key to the outside door of the 19th century majestic but decaying apartment block where we lived, I noticed a man struggling across the pavement towards me, uncomfortably clutching an umbrella. I recognised Luigi, one of Beni's friends.

"Shanna, can I come in? I need to speak to you and leave a message for Beni".

We went in together but I sensed something was wrong. Luigi would never come around to our house when I was alone out of respect for Beni. This was Sicilian protocol; it was an unwritten rule but respected by all. Luigi came into the apartment and I offered him a towel to dry his hair whilst I made some espresso coffee for us. We sat awkwardly on hard chairs in our small dining-room waiting for the volatile coffeepot to spit coffee over my newly cleaned cooker. Beni and I had numerous arguments over the right quantities of coffee and water that went into the coffee pot for the best blend. We disagreed over whether or not a frayed rubber washer sandwiched between the two detachable sections of the coffee pot was the underlying cause of its erratic behaviour. But each time we went shopping, neither of us remembered to replace the rubber washer. Our domestic arguments usually ended up with Beni lamenting:

"Shanna, I can't believe your mother didn't teach you these things. Every woman knows how to iron a man's shirt and make the coffee."

"What nonsense Beni! I didn't have an Italian mother or a Jewish mother to teach me anything practical. The only thing my mother was capable of teaching me was how to drink a bottle of sherry in half an hour."

We usually ended up laughing at this with my promising to do better in the future. Fortunately, Beni had a sense of humour.

Luigi and I sat at the table and he heaped two teaspoons of sugar into his espresso coffee. With averted eyes he suddenly muttered in a low voice, "Beni's life is in danger, Shanna. He has been warned not to write the article he is writing on 'C' and to stop all further journalistic investigations".

I looked at him incredulously. "How do you know this?"

"Never mind. 'They' asked me to tell him this. He must stop… or else."

"Can you not go the police?" I could tell by his expression that I had made an inane remark unworthy of my academic status. "No, I realise you can't. What do I do then?"

He leaned towards me earnestly and whispered as if the four walls had ears: "Tell him to stop investigating this case and ask him to leave Palermo. Please Shanna. This is serious... there are people who want Beni dead."

I suddenly became aware of the seriousness of Beni's situation and it hit me like a thunderbolt. I said I would speak to Beni. After Luigi had left, I rang Beni at his office. He sounded busy but in a bright mood and enthusiastic about some article he was writing on a particular breed of dogs that had just been introduced to Sicily. He said he would be home at the weekend. Because he was so upbeat, I decided not to mention Luigi's visit and wondered whether the whole thing was really a bit of a storm in a coffee cup. Sicily abounded with stories of mafia, corruption and conspiracy theories, over half of them untrue. I decided I would speak to Beni about it when he returned home on the weekend.

Luigi and his wife Marta rang us the following week, inviting us to their smallholding in the country on Sunday. They said they were planning a barbecue. The couple made their own brand of local wine on their tiny farm and grew all their own vegetables. Marta said she would bring along some meat to cook and on my instigation, asked us to bring some speciality Sicilian pastries. We had been to the farm a couple of times before and we knew the directions. It was about thirty kilometres from Catania and we arrived at the farm on the outskirts of a small town called Palagonia around midday. We were welcomed enthusiastically and Luigi had already started to prepare the barbeque coals for the fire. Marta had the meat marinating in oil and lemon juice whilst she chopped up the salad. She told me where to find the tablecloth and cutlery to set the table. I hoped she had brought table napkins so as not to upset Beni. Naturally, she had. Sicilian women never forgot those sorts of things! Thinking back over that day and re-visiting and re-analysing and re-playing it again and again in my mind, every scene, every snippet of information, every word and every picture, Marta appeared no different to any other time I had known her. However, Luigi was edgy and I wondered whether it had anything to do with his visit to me and uncertainty of how Beni would react when he knew. Beni had not been too keen on coming here but I had convinced him of its merit believing Luigi would seize this opportunity to discuss the personal danger issues with him. I felt it was better if they came from Luigi as Beni was often dismissive of my advice.

Luigi offered to take us for a short walk before lunch and Marta asked us to collect some fennel growing in the little adjacent allotment for the salad. We set off walking in a southerly direction, towards the part of their land that confined with a large stretch of communal wasteland used by the military in their training exercises. The land was surrounded by barbed wire with large notices in red paint threatening: 'DANGER. MILITARY MANOEUVRES IN PROGRESS. KEEP OUT'. I vaguely heard Luigi mumble something about forgetting to give Marta instructions regarding the lighting of the barbeque and he unexpectedly took off at speed in the direction of the farmhouse. As he left, somewhat hesitantly I noted in retrospect, he indicated the area where the allotment was situated. I slipped my left arm through Beni's, my free right hand pointing towards the spot where I believed I saw the fennel. At that spilt second a man suddenly emerged in front us as if from nowhere. In spite of the oppressive heat, he was dressed in the style of a traditional Sicilian farmer. He wore gaiters, black boots, a black jacket and black 'coppola' (a particular type of Sicilian cloth cap). He was carrying the Sicilian hunting gun, the 'lupara'. Beni froze in horror and jerked his arm away from mine. The scene that followed was enacted in slow motion and was to remain etched in my memory forever. Beni yelled 'No' and lashed out, pushing me away from him with such force that I lost my balance temporarily, crying out in fear as I reeled backwards. I saw the pain and fear in Beni's eyes as they looked into mine like a wounded animal. I saw the man draw the rifle towards his shoulder; I saw him pull back the trigger and shoot Beni at point blank range. I felt the explosion and ricochet of the bullet as it shattered Beni's skull causing his body to keel backwards in timeless involuntary motion. I witnessed in horror my tee-shirt change from yellow to vivid crimson with Beni's blood. Somebody was screaming, screaming, screaming. There was a crater full of blood where there should have been a face. I had lost control; I was dying. Someone was screaming, screaming, screaming. People were running, shouting, sirens were wailing. I passed out, aware of nothing more.

Chapter 15

Music: *Hotel California*, The Eagles (1976)

"Eh, signorina eh...let's go back over the story again. There is much that is unconvincing here."

I was being interrogated at a police station in Catania. I still wore the once yellow tee shirt dyed scarlet by Beni's blood, but they had allowed me to wash my face and hands. The interrogation room was small and shabby with narrow grid-like windows very high up and almost touching the discoloured ceiling. I vaguely remember seeing a Pirelli poster of a beautiful nude girl draped erotically around a snake. There was a senior police officer ('Carabiniere') and two others of a more junior rank.

"Why am I here?", I asked for the umpteenth time, "I've told you everything. I'm exhausted. Why can't I go home?"

"But you have not told us everything", said the senior officer pedantically. "Your friends Luigi and Marta Zappala maintain it was your idea to have a picnic at their farm today. **You** are saying it was their idea."

I felt I was losing contact with reality and fully expected to see a dormouse leap out of a teapot at any minute. Time stood still; the regular beat of the ticking wall clock cut across the silence informing me that I was still sane. The tiny room was unbearably warm and airless and the senior officer yanked his handkerchief out of his pocket and mopped his brow continuously.

"Tell me again signorina, whose idea was it to visit Palagonia?"

I kept asking for a lawyer and eventually someone was called but his English was poor and even incomprehensible at times so I insisted on their calling the British Consul in Palermo. Being a Sunday, he was nowhere to be found. To my dismay, arrangements were made to detain me overnight and although my conversational Italian was more than adequate, I was unfamiliar with formal legal jargon and its implications for my detention. My lawyer told me I would spend the night in a women's prison.

"Why?", I cried out in exhausted disbelief.

"Signorina, you are being charged with the murder of Benedetto Scalia."

I spent the night in a filthy little prison cell. I was fortunate I had a cell to myself, but I learned that this was by special arrangement and due to the fact that I was a foreigner. The lavatory inside my cell was blocked and it stank so much I kept retching from the stench. I was unable to sleep, traumatised by the happenings of the day. I felt as if all emotion had frozen in time and I was looking at myself from afar, dissociated from my physical being. I functioned in a dream-like state, oblivious to everything except to the wretched stench in my cell. I had mentally shut down. The following morning the vice-consul arrived from Palermo, the consul being on annual leave. The vice-consul and I took an immediate dislike to one another. I perceived him as 'the old school tie' British snob from a minor public school with a peculiar dress sense (known locally as 'Englishman in cork-up-arse look') that Sicilians loved to sneer at. He perceived me as the product of the new generation meritocracy with radical ideas that menaced the status quo and with the morals of an alley cat. He took it upon himself to criticise my 'fraternisation with the natives'. Mr Harding wore a dark suit, white nylon shirt and narrow red and white striped necktie that threatened to throttle him if he indulged in a sudden jerk of the head. He was sweating profusely in 34 degrees centigrade but the weather did not affect his conventional choice of attire or entice him to wear a cotton shirt and ditch the school tie. He was tall and bony with large owl-like spectacles. He was aged about thirty-five but he looked and sounded like a much older man.

"They want to know your movements over the past six weeks. Did you visit Palermo at all? Who did you speak to outside of the University staff?"

"Am I on trial here?"

"No. But you will need to co-operate. You were known to be having an affair with the deceased. What do you say to that?"

"Nothing. I was living with him. I… loved him."

Silence. Feelings cannot be acknowledged by Mr Harding; empathy belongs to lesser beings.

"They found your passport when they searched your flat in Catania. They say you did not go to England the second week of August as you claim. Your passport is not stamped on that date."

"Maybe they didn't stamp it. I can't remember", I replied listlessly.

"They would have stamped your passport", he pontificated coldly. He pursed his thin lips and this gesture triggered a strong reaction in me: anger at my situation, anger at injustice, anger at the years of the British class system that devoured my confidence as a child. The Italians had nothing comparable with it which was why I fitted in here and never felt so socially ostracized as I had in my own country. I felt years of repressed anger draining through me like a poison and repositioning itself like a warhead against the ineffectual necktie in front of me.

"Get out of here, you pompous pratt", I cried, "Get out NOW!"

With his face flushed red from rage and embarrassment, he rose abruptly and left the interrogation room provided by the prison service. "And do your bloody job and find me a fuckin' lawyer that can speak English."

"No need for filthy language", he muttered as he left.

When reality dawned that I would be spending another night in jail, in the same blood-soaked clothes, in the same stinking cell, I began to sob uncontrollably. I was ignored. Later on in the morning someone brought me a coffee and two white pills which I was told were tranquillizers. I took a chance and swallowed them as I wanted to feel less anxious, confused and exhausted. That same day, I was re-interviewed by the police but this time with my lawyer present. They focussed a number of questions on my 'alleged' trip to England. This time I told them the truth. I had been in Sardinia with a lover and was guilty of hiding that piece of information from them. I was trying to protect my reputation. That was all, nothing more; nothing less.

The three uniformed 'Carabinieri' enjoyed every minute of this disclosure, confirming the popular belief of their Sicilian mothers that all English women were whores. The lawyer then put a proposition to me whilst only the senior officer was present in the room. Would I be prepared to testify that Beni had been shot on the military land next to Luigi's property? Would I be prepared to say that he passed from Luigi's property to the military area believing it was safe to do so? If I agreed to sign such a declaration, I could leave the prison now. If not, they would keep me another twenty-four hours before considering bail. I was stupefied by their proposal and mentally fought to understand why they wanted me to do this and what difference it would make to their accusations and my present predicament.

Then I understood.

They were going to change Beni's death from 'an assassination' to 'an accident' and I, as the one and only eyewitness, was to be instrumental in helping them do this. Beni would be doubly betrayed as no one would ever be arrested for his murder. The mafia had got him in the end as Luigi said they would. Luigi? What part had he played in inviting us to his property? He had lied saying the plan to meet that weekend had come from me. Why had he lied? Why had he come to forewarn me some days before? None of it made any sense. He had been trying to caution us but he had not given me the full facts. Had he and his family been threatened? I had not even briefed Beni, believing it would have upset him and spoiled our weekend together. How ridiculously wanting that belief seemed now!

"No", I said. "Never. I will not lie. I want justice for Beni's murder. I will never accept anything less. I will not lie."

"Then you will stay here", said the lawyer with a frown.

"I will stay here", I reiterated firmly. "But I will get justice form the British Government at least. You cannot hold me indefinitely."

"Signorina, Mr Scalia is dead. You can do nothing. What has that man from the British Consulate done but annoy you? Sign the declaration and you can go. You can attend your friend's funeral and mourn his death". The chief Carabiniere added, "what does a lovely woman like you want to stay here in prison for...eh?" he ventured with a shrug, mopping his dripping brow for the umpteenth time.

"No", I said stubbornly, "I will not sign. Never."

My friend Maria-Pia, one of the women I used to share a flat with before moving in with Beni, visited me that same evening together with her lawyer boyfriend, Gianni. She brought me a change of clothes, saying she couldn't believe they were still holding me without charge. Gianni whispered to me through the visitor's grille that my situation was serious indeed and that the press had got hold of the story and there were journalists and photographers outside the prison waiting to interview me. The story would hit the papers as there were circulating rumours of conspiracy, corruption at the top, murder and betrayal. The sort of thing librettos of grand operas are based on and the bread and butter of tabloid journalists desperate for a story. It began to dawn on me that I could not control events and they were sweeping me along with a terrifying tidal force, as the River Usk had done those many years ago. I felt I was drowning again but this time there was no ledge on which to rest my feet and no friends to save me. Gianni resolutely advised me to sign whatever they wanted and retract the statement later, at least I could get out of prison. I said I would consider it. That evening, my third incarcerated, I received a phone call from the private secretary of Lord Tressington, the owner of the Lion Rock villa in Sardinia where Hal and I had spent that glorious clandestine week together - another time, another world. We got off to the wrong start as after stating his name he immediately drawled:

"I understand you stayed in Lord T's villa in Sardinia. His Lordship would request that such information should not be made public." He carried on talking but I was emotionally numb as if the conversation did not apply to me at all. I was aware only of how his voice and manner irritated me.

"Why don't you ask his lordship to do his own dirty work and ask me himself. I don't speak to minions. Read 'La Sicilia' for the lurid details of Lion Rock tomorrow!"

I slammed down the phone feeling better than I had over the past forty-eight hours, tranquillizers notwithstanding. His lordship telephoned within twenty minutes apologising for his secretary's abruptness. He then began a well-constructed argument, calmly pointing out that although he owned the villa where I had stayed, it did not implicate him personally in Beni's murder. Instead, it would implicate Mr Stanton. The villa was given as a perk to senior management and designated shareholders of the company, and in this instance on the understanding it was for Mr Stanton's family, not his mistress, if I understood his meaning. Disclosure of Mr Stanton's whereabouts in August would have personal and professional implications for him. Once the story hit the press, all my dirty linen and Mr Stanton's would become public knowledge, if I followed his drift. He sympathetically advised me to make the choice I could best live with. If it was fame I was after, this kind of notoriety was as transitory as the Profumo Affair bore witness. The names of many of the individuals implicated in the notorious political scandal of the 1960s could not even be recalled nowadays. On the other hand, damage to professional and personal lives had been irreparable. By the time I put the phone down I already knew I would sign. For all my fine talk about fighting Sicilian corruption, I had betrayed Beni just like all the others. I had betrayed Beni to protect Hal. I was no different to anybody else. I was as vulnerable to corruption as the next person, only far less honest about it. I had a lot to learn about myself.

That same evening, I left Catania Prison without any formal charges being brought against me. The following morning, they released Beni's body for burial.

Chapter 16

Music: *'Cavatina',* John Williams (1979)

Maria Pia was kind enough to offer accommodation at her summer residence in the village of Acitrezza. Her apartment was situated on the second floor of a three-storey block near the sea and along the eastern coastal road in the direction of Taormina. The village was renowned for its three steep lava rocks rising starkly from the smooth calm of the gentle bay and pointing upwards to the sky. It was said to mark the spot where in Greek mythology, Ulysses had defeated the Cyclops. The one-eyed giant chased Ulysses and his men howling in rage. It stopped only to hurl three gargantuan lava boulders into the sea to prevent their escape by sinking their ship. From my bedroom window in Maria-Pia's apartment, I had a magnificent view of the three jagged rocks in the bay, but I was unaware of anything much at this time, just dragging myself through a day took considerable effort. I had been asked to stay away from the funeral by Beni's family. A third party visited Maria-Pia's house for the specific purpose of sounding me out. I agreed in principle but I said I would at least like to join the mourners along the route to the crematorium. My hosts were uneasy but agreed to drive me there. The funeral service was held on a Thursday in one of the oldest churches in Catania, in the area of the city where Beni's family lived. The main Via Etnea was closed to traffic as the funeral cortege drew slowly down it. The 'Commune' only ever closed the Via Etnea for funerals of high-ranking individuals in politics or in the military. On this momentous and grave occasion, Beni Scalia was clearly more important in death than he had been in life. Onlookers bowed their heads as the hearse drew by. The whole of Sicily knew why Beni Scalia had been murdered. No one believed the official line in the newspapers that lamented the fact that he had been shot in error by a stray bullet in the military zone. What they did not know was the role I had played in the drama. I had been mentioned in passing as an English friend of Luigi and Marta Zappala. There was no information to link me to Beni in any way.

The silent cortege passed down the long avenue of the local cemetery lined by tall conifers and plane trees. The road suddenly widened to provide a stopping place for the hearse whilst the coffin was solemnly removed and carried into the chapel. Beni's parents and his sister swathed in black walked behind the hearse and behind them other close relatives. Although she wore a black veil, I caught a glimpse of his mother's face white and swollen from crying. She passed by me and stared ahead into nothingness. Neither she nor his sister acknowledged my presence. "God bless you, my love", I said silently as the coffin decked in floral displays passed majestically by. I pondered on how Beni, a committed atheist, would have viewed all this spectacle. "May you rest in peace and forgive me for what I have done. Goodbye Beni, goodbye." Out of respect for his parents' wishes, I did not attend the short service at the crematorium but returned home with Gianni and Maria Pia.

Later that evening, I walked to one of the Roman Catholic churches in Acitrezza, dodging around the pavement ice-cream sellers and the myriad tables set out for al fresco dining. The rich odour of diverse pizza fillings wafted into the air. The church I chose was open every evening and on entry I smelled the incense and it stung my eyes. A few elderly women were gabbling prayers to the right of the church where a small area was set aside for lighting candles and meditation. A huge plaster figure of Jesus Christ hung above the alter. The statue was embossed in gold leaf and it had piercing blue eyes that stared blankly, dripping vermilion from underneath a lopsided crown of thorns. I shuddered at the image and it disturbed me so much that I made a hasty retreat and hurried home along the panoramic road running parallel to the sea. I went back to the apartment and straight to the balcony outside my bedroom. I lit a cigarette and stood silently watching the panoramic scene ahead of me. The moon hung low over the water highlighting shadowy shapes of fishermen in trawlers retrieving their fishing nets from the sea. I could vaguely discern the figures of men in the light from the boats as they swerved their flashlights backwards and forwards and hauled up their day's catch from the water. I looked at the scene with an all-consuming desire of release from emotional pain. I felt my heart would explode. I prayed aloud:

"Dear God, if there is a God, please forgive me. Beni forgive me because I can never forgive myself. Dearest God, I will change, I promise". The Rev. Morgan Morgan's sermon on Delilah sprang to mind. I was an adulterous woman and a cowardly one. I was continuing a relationship with a married man and about to be the cause of the break-up of his marriage. I had continued to see Hal in spite of all the warnings from my friends and my own better judgement. I had had an abortion which had damaged my body and made any future childbearing excessively difficult. I had betrayed the man who had asked me to marry him and besmirched his good name. How could such a woman respect herself or ever forgive herself for the havoc she had wreaked in the lives of others? I swore to God that I would make amends. I would end my relationship with Hal. I would not see him again. I would leave Sicily as soon as possible. My Catania friends were pleading with me to do this as they pointed out that my life could be in danger if I remained in Sicily. I had been an eyewitness to Beni's murder and had glimpsed the assassin. I clenched my hands and cried out, gasping for breath and emitting uncontrollable heaving sobs into the night air.

"Please forgive me, please, please."

Suddenly, from nowhere, flashed into my mind a vision of my grandmother and I cried out desperately to her. How I envied the simple life of the fishermen of Acitrezza, free of the torment I was currently experiencing. Part of me wondered whether I ever would be free of confusing thoughts and inner turmoil. My personality had depended so much on love of novelty and impulsive choice making. I wanted and craved stability but realised I would have to change radically to achieve the things that appeared so obvious and natural to other people. At some visceral level I became aware of what I needed to do. I looked out across the bay at the fishermen of Acitrezza, trying to quell the engulfing emotions of guilt and crushing emptiness. I would need to change in order to survive.

The University agreed to pay me until Christmas even if I terminated my contract immediately and did not work out my period of notice. The problem was that it would take months for me to be paid and I realised that I had very little money left. I was not good with money and had saved little in spite of adding to my salary by providing private English Literature lessons. I also needed to find accommodation in one of the most expensive cities in the world. I hoped I could stay with Anna for a little while until I found my feet but knew that her flatmate would start whinging if I stayed too long as there was not really the space for three women and their belongings. I went around to the apartment in Catania that I had shared with Beni for the last two years. Maria-Pia accompanied me. Someone had removed all of Beni's clothes and personal effects and the apartment was clear of everything apart from my possessions. We bundled them quickly into the suitcases we had brought with us, both of us feeling uneasy there. It was as if I had not been part of Beni's life and yet here was cooker with the little espresso maker at the side; the one we argued over. This was the bed we had shared; there was the inadequate wardrobe with a broken hinge. I saw these things but at the same time, I did not see them. I did not want to be reminded of my past life with Beni. It was less than two weeks ago that we had eaten, argued and made love in this apartment. It felt as if the present had erased all trace of the past. Time had hurtled by, leaving us grabbing wildly for the old reality. I did not want the memories to overshadow and overwhelm me. They had to be buried with Beni.

I found the ruby and diamond ring Beni had given me when he proposed on the fateful day of my return from England. I put the ring in my pocket. Although I was desperately short of money I knew I would not keep it. I had made up my mind to return it to Carmela, Beni's sister. Finally, we finished clearing the flat and Gianni arrived at the door to help us shift the stuff down the stairs. I locked the door of the apartment for the last time. As I did, I had a flashback - I saw Beni standing on the stairs calling out, "Shanna, don't lock the keys inside! I have forgotten mine again."

I wrote a cold letter to Hal at his office. I plainly stated that I would be staying on in Italy and I had decided not to see him again. I begged him not ever to attempt to contact me as I needed to move on with my life which I would not be able to do that if we kept in contact with one another. I wrote the letter as if I were someone else writing to Hal. I could not trust the luxury of feelings and indeed at that moment in time I was able to access very few. I knew Hal would comply after receiving my letter. I also wrote a brief note of condolence to Carmela, Beni's sister and returned Beni's ring to her. A few days later she telephoned and asked whether she could meet me briefly, expressing a wish to see me before I left for England. She arrived dressed in the traditional black mourning. I felt awkward as we drank coffee together at Maria-Pia's house.

I thought I had better be open with her as I had nothing more to lose anyway. "I'm so sorry about Beni…doing what I did."

"You had to. They put so much pressure on you. We understand as we are Sicilian. You could not have done anything different."

I began to feel that I missed something here and that we were not quite moving on the same track. I was silent.

She went on: "We know they threatened your family."

In a flash, the penny dropped. Beni's family knew nothing about Hal and the Sardinia affair. It had been kept from them. They had learned of some threats to me or at least *had assumed* there would be threats. At that moment I wanted to shout thanks to God for sparing them and Beni this final hurt, anger and humiliation. For once I did not care about myself. I embraced Carmela. "Thank you", I said. "I do so wish things could have been different."

"So do I", she said, choking back her tears, "so do I."

Ten days later I took a flight from Catania airport to London. I never returned to Sicily again.

Chapter 17

Music: *'We are the Champions',* Queen (1977)

On my return to England the previous year, I had stayed with Anna in Kensal Rise for a couple of weeks before moving to a bedsitter in Kilburn, Northwest London. I managed to find full time work at a private college in Central London where I taught English as a Foreign Language to overseas students. The college paid well. I was fortunate to find such a well-paid job so quickly. I was lonely in my bedsit but I spent every weekend over at Anna's as I knew very few people in London. The few university friends I had had were now married with children and had moved out of Greater London to more affordable areas in the suburbs. Others had returned to the towns and villages of their origins and some were working overseas. There were few single people around North London whom I knew or wanted to frequent socially. After my return to England, I became quite ill with very anxious thoughts and symptoms of paranoia. I kept thinking people were following me or looking at me strangely. I also had terrible nightmares and would wake up sweating and shaking. Once when travelling on a bus, I feared I would have a panic attack and I had to get off immediately gasping for breath. A kind passer-by in Oxford Street called an ambulance where I was taken to hospital. I was discharged within an hour of my ECG results and told I was suffering from a severe anxiety attack with attenuating symptoms of panic. It was suggested I spoke to my GP about treatment. I thoroughly disliked my GP as he had refused to prescribe any additional tranquillizers so I was smoking more cannabis weed than I could afford and had also started to use alcohol to self-medicate. Anna came to my rescue and 'fiddled the paperwork' so that I got assessed quickly by a clinical psychologist at the hospital where she worked. It was the beginning of my slow recovery to 'normal life' whatever that was. I saw the psychologist weekly and then fortnightly for roughly six months. She then recommended psychotherapy for the issues I had with my parents, with a particular focus on my childhood sadness and loneliness revolving around befuddled family dynamics and lack of a robust parental figure. However, there was about a two-year waiting list for psychotherapy and I could not afford to go privately. But I had made some positive changes to my lifestyle. I stopped smoking cannabis altogether and limited my alcohol use. The pills had long gone as my stubborn GP still refused to prescribe. I had lost my temper with him once when he had been firmer than usual with me about prescribing Valium but I am so grateful now that I did not end up addicted to benzodiazepines like my mother and many of my acquaintances since.

Anna was finally getting married. The wedding was to be in early November in Israel and I had planned to go because for once I was not insolvent and owing money to Anna. My mother and Theodore had finally agreed to sell the infamous piece of land and buy Davy Cottage together. Unbeknown to me, my grandparents had left half the field to me so my mother and Theodore would have to compensate me financially for the sale of the land. They sold at a healthy profit because of the land's availability of planning permission, a rarity in those parts. The district of Foistneth was a National Park area with very tight building controls so any land sold with available planning permission commanded a very high premium indeed. I used my share of the money to put down a small deposit on a very pleasant but small two-bedroom flat in comfortable walking distance of Finchley Road underground station in Northwest London. I had my first mortgage and I had done it all alone, but of course with a great deal of help from my grandmother. I kept some money back for Anna's wedding and we spent hours discussing the places I would visit in Israel and whether I could find 'a nice Jewish man with a professional background' to make a life with. Inevitably talk of mixed faith marriages took us to reminiscences and Ruby Weiz's mother got a mention, together with the 'shiksa' that Joe the dentist was hiding from his mother. These were once again days of normality; the calm after the storm.

Anna finished working for the National Health Service at the end of August and went home to Cardiff to make preparations for her wedding before her departure to Israel the third week of October. She would fly out two weeks after Yom Kippur. I would join her and her family the last week of October and would be met by Dr Klein at Tel Aviv airport. But none of this happened; none of it. On 6th October on Yom Kippur, Egypt and Syria launched a coordinated attack on the

Suez and Golan fronts, taking Israel by surprise. Yossi was called up to fight for his country and died in action during the battle for the Golan Heights. His family called the Kleins and Anna prepared herself to travel to Israel for her lover's funeral rather than for their wedding. When I spoke to her over the telephone in Cardiff, she was distraught with grief. Remembering her former eating disorder, I feared her ability to cope. But Anna, like myself, was a survivor. She returned to London immediately after the funeral in spite of Juliet's remonstrations and moved into the Finchley Road flat with me. Needless to say, I had cancelled my earlier trip to Israel.

Anna and I cried a lot together as I re-lived memories of Beni's death which uncannily was almost a year to the day of Yosse's death. I disclosed to Anna about Hal and Sardinia, followed within weeks by Beni's cruel and untimely death. Talking helped her. She said:

"At least Yossi died a hero's death. He died knowing I loved him and there was nothing I could have done to stop it happening. Oh God, Sian. How long does this pain last? If I wake up in the night I think of Yossi; if I'm walking along the street and I see a young dark-haired man who doesn't even look like him, I think it's Yossi. I have crazy thoughts like… perhaps he is really working undercover for Mossad and he faked his own death because he decided not to marry me but couldn't bring himself to tell me. I sometimes venture the thought that his family have gone to all the trouble of burying someone else to make it look authentic. I think I'm going mad, Sian."

"I know my love", I sobbed, "I know, I know. That's what loss feels like. There's no short cut to pain relief Anna. We just have to go through it one day at a time." Sometimes I believed I should have been the psychologist.

Wilf died of a heart attack at the beginning of 1974 and Dora sold 'the caff' and moved into a tiny bungalow on the outskirts of Foistneth, very close to her sister Brenda the Boast. The two sisters quarrelled a lot but it did not stop them from going to bingo together. Pearl was desperately unhappy within her marriage but she had nowhere to run to with two small children especially since Dora had moved to the bungalow. Dean had left home and had been living openly as a gay man in Newport for some years, much to Wilf and Dora's great shame.

When Wilf died, he had not spoken to his son for over three years. According to Wilf, "a pooftah is worse than an unmarried mother." Dora said she blamed Mick Jagger (one assumes the Rolling Stones' music) but Wilf did not blame Jagger. He blamed Dean and 'the silent treatment' of Dean continued until he died.

As predicted, Kevin lost the family home. He did not keep up the mortgage repayments due to his constant job changing and financial schemes which backfired and left him penniless. They were evicted from their flat by the mortgagor bank. Kevin found a temporary home on a caravan site in Chelmsford. The site was crowded with people, children and dogs and the caravan itself was dirty with cheap, threadbare furnishings. The children cried a lot there especially Dylan, causing Kevin to shout and threaten, terrifying the child. Dylan was very clingy and socially withdrawn. He screamed when Pearl took him to school in Chelmsford and wouldn't stop crying for a whole morning. He had already started school in Forest Hill and had been there seven months before their latest move. It had taken a while for him to settle in at the Forest Hill primary school; now he had to face a new environment all over again. Within three weeks of their move, Pearl rang me and begged for help.

"I can't stand it anymore Sian, I'm at breaking point", her voice shook uncontrollably in a way that was very uncharacteristic of Pearl.

"Please help me."

One weekday afternoon, when Pearl assured me that Kevin was not at home, I took a day off work and drove to Chelmsford in a hired car to collect her and the children. I was shocked at the conditions they were living in and the state of the children. They both looked pale and skinny and neither child smiled at me. Dylan hid behind his mother's chair and could only be coaxed out with sweets. Pearl had already bundled some of their toys and clothes into suitcases so that we would not lose time. Kevin could arrive back any minute and stop them leaving. I noticed Pearl had a red weal across her face. "Does he hit you?" I asked shocked. He had not seemed the type. There again, what is the type?

"Sometimes", she said, "he says it's my fault as I make him angry. He never used to Sian, really. It's only recently he's started hitting me."

"So that makes it all right I suppose", I mumbled, pushing down the steps of the caravan and towards my car with a loose stack of children's toys and books in my arms. We had hardly got back to the Finchley Road flat when Kevin rang, angrily demanding to speak to Pearl. I heard him shouting on the phone saying he was coming around to collect her. Pearl told him 'no' and at that point I grabbed the telephone, telling him I would call the police if he harassed us.

He didn't come round but he kept ringing my number all night so I had to take the phone off the hook.

Kevin continued to harass us by telephone and one day when I was at work he came to the flat and shouted through the intercom. My flat was one of four on the second floor of a converted house. A Chinese family lived in the flat below and the woman, believing Kevin to be a drunk, shouted at him to go away or she would call the police. Pearl feared going out even to buy milk. I suggested she went to the police and took out an injunction against Kevin and then begin divorce proceedings. "I don't know if I can do that yet", Pearl hedged. "Also, what happens when Anna decides to come back from Cardiff? There's not enough room here for all of us." Since officially handing in her notice, Anna now only did locum work in London but she had applied for permanent work in the children's service at a hospital in Birmingham. Her interview was at the end of April. I tried to reassure Pearl that Anna could and would stay elsewhere and that it was more important that she broke away from Kevin for both her own and the children's sake.

I let Pearl and the children have the bigger bedroom but we were very pushed for space. There were clothes and toys everywhere with the sink constantly full of dirty dishes. But we battled on in a good cause. On Anna's return to London, she went to stay temporarily with her relatives in Golders Green. In the evening, when the children were in bed she would come over to the flat and join us in a bottle of wine and conversations about feminism. By now, I too had read Germaine Greer's 'The Female Eunuch'. We all three related to many of the issues raised. I felt angered by my own beliefs that I had been put on this earth 'to please a man' and not even my university education had managed to override these entrenched cultural mores. Because of her particular education and her avid desire for knowledge, Anna was better informed than the two of us. I was trying to catch up and was fast becoming aware of cultural, racial and sexist stereotyping. I saw what the 1950s had done to women and how the 'so called' sexual liberation of the 1960s had not freed women's heads from bondage, only their bodies. I viewed as overrated the popular beliefs of the time surrounding feminist issues. Current opportunities did offer a good forum for discussion - especially for the educated - but in reality it was still very much a man's world.

Kevin waited downstairs in his van in the street while these discussions were going on. He would ring Pearl and sob over the telephone how much he loved her and wanted his children back. Then he would threaten to kill her, the children, or himself. Once he rang up when drunk and threatened to kill me. Both of us advised Pearl not to have contact with him and leave all correspondence to her solicitor. Dylan had started yet another new school on Finchley Road.

Then the inevitable happened.

I returned home from work one afternoon to find Pearl and the children gone. There was a scribbled note on the table saying:

> *Hello Sian and Anna,*
>
> *I'm sorry about this but it is the best for all concerned. Kevin has found a new place for us, a house in Croydon. I know we are in the way here as the flat is small for all of us but thank you both so much for everything. Another thing, I am pregnant again and feel I cannot go through a termination. Kevin wants me back and he is the father of my children.*
>
> *Thank you. I love you both. I don't know what I'd do without you.*
>
> *Love Pearl.*

I screamed with rage when I read this and immediately telephoned Steve Palmer, a clinical psychologist friend of Anna's. We had just started dating. He tried to calm me down and ended up coming over to my flat bringing an Indian takeaway for both of us. I said I couldn't believe Pearl would do this to her children after all the emotional upheaval they had been through. He said women do that sort of thing for years, even when the man has half battered them to death. They only leave when they, themselves, reach a certain attitude to change. It cannot be directly pre-empted by others. Well-meaning families and friends are setting themselves up for disappointment if they believe the victim will move permanently before she is ready. I phoned Anna and she said more or less the same thing although even she had believed that Pearl would not return to Kevin. She had stayed with us seven weeks and we really felt Kevin was out of her system. How little we understand the anthropological and psychological attachment of human beings, although some might argue that cultural conditioning has an equal role to play with biology in human attachment. Because of my difficulty in coming to terms with the situation, I booked myself some private therapy with a psychotherapist in Hampstead.

CHAPTER 18

Music: *'Coming In From The Cold'*, Bob Marley and The Wailers (1984)

One evening in early July I received a telephone call from Anna. She said she was going to get married. I was unaware she was seeing anyone seriously so I was stunned by her sudden disclosure. She stated in her familiar calm and detached voice that her marriage would take place within the next couple of months but she needed to speak to discuss it with me because she needed my help. Her request intrigued me because of the lack of excitement and enthusiasm in her voice, usually present when breaking news to friends about a prospective wedding. Anna went on to ask me to accompany her to Cardiff so that she could break the news to her parents in person which immediately red flagged 'an issue' in my book. I urgently wanted to know about the man she intended marrying but she said she would discuss it with me at another time; it was complicated. Could we book a date to drive to Cardiff together and discuss it along the way? I congratulated her enthusiastically but the secrecy of the affair was a cause for concern. I speculated that either her intended was a divorcee with children or non-Jewish, both of which would cause anguish to Anna's parents. But Anna had often said that Juliet would prefer her to marry a Jewish divorcee than a single 'goy' (non-Jewish man) so I desperately hoped for Anna's sake that it would not be the latter.

Anna had moved to Birmingham some years earlier and was enthusiastic about her new role within the Children's Psychology Service. She was working with children and young people who had been traumatised, either by parental or carer abuse or by witnessing shocking experiences as refugees that contributed to psychological trauma. Anna sent me some literature on this and I found myself relating to the numb feelings and painful physical sensations I had struggled with after the trauma of Beni's assassination that fateful afternoon in Sicily. I identified with the shutting down of the psyche. I identified with the subsequent anxious thoughts and feelings of panic.

I loved to discuss these matters with Steve Palmer because as a clinical psychologist, he had much greater understanding of human behaviour than I had. I had become very close to Steve, particularly over the past two years and at one point he had asked me to marry him. I was full of doubt and 'ummed and ahhed' about it as there were so many things I was unsure about in our relationship. I was now thirty-one and unmarried. It was difficult for me to have children so I would need to start fairly soon to have any sort of surgery possibly to be followed by fertility treatment or I would miss the age cohort recommended for treatment which was under thirty-five. Steve had an eight-year-old son who lived in Australia with his ex-partner and he saw his son once a year on average. He was adamant that he was not particularly interested in having more children but I still felt this was unfair on him. Steve and I enjoyed doing many things together: meals out, cinema, art galleries, theatre, walks in Regent's Park and over Primrose Hill. But our sex life lacked passion and Steve's libido was low compared to the other two significant men in my life. I was determined to put both Beni and Hal out of my mind. It was different times, I was now older, I felt differently about life, my needs and expectations were less intense. I asked myself many times whether sex should predominate in a relationship and was not compatibility more important?

Steve was average looking. His best feature was undoubtedly his deep-set dark eyes set off to perfection by unusually long lashes. His emotions were very tightly under control (the total opposite of Beni) as if held in check by a coiled spring. I wrongly assumed that this was due to his psychology training. Steve was not as practical as Hal but he did not have expectations about 'a woman's role' and would pitch in with housework and shopping in a way no other man I had known was capable of doing. I felt Steve was very much part of present thinking and new-age philosophy but nevertheless, I experienced some unease about making any long-term commitment. I was annoyed at myself, unable to identify the reason why as we were practically living together. Steve had bought a short lease on his flat in West Hampstead and I had a long lease on mine in the Finchley Road area. His flat was double the size of mine so we spent more time at his place. But I liked to return to my own home because it gave me a sense of freedom. I was not beholden to anyone. I had somewhere permanent to live and a decent teaching job to sustain me. Most of my life had been plagued by shortage of money, lack of permanent accommodation and temporary work contracts.

Over the past year I had taken qualifications in the Teaching of English As A Foreign Language (TEFL) funded by the college where I worked. By sheer chance due to a surprise encounter with a friend of a friend followed by a subsequent recommendation, I found a new job with a publishing company in central London and entered the arena of writing and publishing TEFL materials for overseas business students. I really enjoyed the change of work from teaching overseas students to researching different professions for typical English vocabulary and colloquial expressions most used. This undertaking was focussed on non-native speakers of English to familiarise them with specialist language norms before undertaking a British qualification of their choice. 'Dr Livingstone I presume' and 'How to trim Martha's hedgerows' (a whole chapter in one of my old teaching books) were superfluous as students of the many nationalities I taught needed English to learn about commerce, shipping law and computer science.

I was eventually promoted to head of my division in the academic publishing company when my manager retired on the grounds of ill health. I was very creative within my speciality, not overly ambitious which paradoxically worked in my favour and perhaps was the explanation for why I made career quickly. I was loyal to my superiors, hard-working, and was not perceived as a threat in the politics of the workplace. Consequently, I did not *nurture* the idea of relinquishing my independence for domestic intimacy even though there were times when I felt lonely in London and very socially isolated. The melancholy words of the Beatles' song 'Eleanor Rigby' came frequently to mind when charging to and from the workplace on the London Underground with averted eyes. If you mistakenly glance at people on the tube they could be crazy enough to start an unnerving conversation.

"All the lonely people, where do they all come from?"

Without Steve I would have been even lonelier. When Anna was in London and I was not working quite as long hours as I was now, I had joined a few social activities at a Liberal Synagogue that Anna attended in Northwest London. I even went to a few services and I found them very moving. The unadorned walls of the synagogue with its Ark in the centre reminded me very much of the Baptist Chapel I had attended as a child. But after Anna left I didn't quite feel I belonged. Although made very welcome, I did not feel I had a role there because I was not intending to convert to Judaism or marry into the faith. Anna was very active on The Council for Christians and Jews and organised social activities and conferences. She continued to be part of these activities when working in Birmingham and on one occasion was interviewed about the aims and working success of the Council for Christians and Jews on Radio 4. She was well informed and spoke without nervousness or hesitation. I felt very proud of her and I missed her a great deal. We had lived together for three years as well as on and off during my early years in Sicily. It was a very big wrench for both of us when we went our separate ways.

I found myself too frequently meeting Steve in the pub after a heavy day at work. Steve was a pub person and he enjoyed sitting for hours drinking and making small talk. I got irritated with this. Drink made me feel tired and I always had the fear it would take hold of me as it had my mother. Steve had no such qualms and said it was the fear in my head that had taken hold of me and I needed a healthy attitude to controlled drinking. He always bought a bottle of wine or a half bottle of vodka to take home with him after the pub.

I had only spoken to Pearl a couple of times since her disappearance from my flat some years before. The family kept moving from rented accommodation to rented accommodation and were currently in Dartford. She had a termination of her third pregnancy as she could not face homelessness again and coping with a young baby. I dreaded to reflect on what all this was doing to Dylan as the little boy would need to keep changing schools. I tried not to think about it but his pinched little face kept coming into my mind. One evening I rang Pearl on the off-chance and was surprised to find the phone had not been cut off - as was not uncommon - and that Pearl answered it directly. She usually waited for a while as she expected it to be someone harassing for money. Pearl said Kevin had left her for another woman ten days ago. She was still in shock but coping. She had wanted to ring me but could not because she felt she had let me down last time and that I despised her for it. Her voice trembled as she tried hard to restrain her sobs. "Sian, I feel desperate. I don't know what to do. The children are now on Social Services 'at risk' register. Kevin has hit the children a couple of times and the school are concerned about Dylan. He is eight and still wetting the bed. They say he's very socially withdrawn at school and he is not learning properly. Jennie is very difficult to control and has kicked one of the teachers. I really struggle for money and sometimes I don't have enough for food as Kevin has taken the children's allowance book and the rent is due at the end of this week. Oh God! We already owe six weeks' rent. I'm really at the end of my tether!"

I talked her through some options, also suggesting that she contact Social Services about allowances for rent and food. I then rang Anna at work and sought advice on Pearl's behalf. I rang Pearl back with Anna's advice but against Anna's advice offered Pearl my flat in Finchley Road after she ventured a half-baked plan of going to Newport and staying with Dean. I said I would live at Steve's for a while. We had considered my letting the Finchley Road flat some time ago. Pearl seized this opportunity thanking me profusely over and over saying that I was a truly wonderful friend. She intimated she would hire a car as they couldn't travel by public transport with all their 'clobber'. Knowing she had no money, I thought this absurd and said I would pick her up sometime early Saturday afternoon. With some of the money from the Foistneth legacy, I had purchased a small second-hand car a few months earlier.

I arrived at Dartford two hours later than predicted as I do not have a logical mind for directions and lost my way many times south of the river. I reached Pearl's house at last and stumbled out of the car feeling hot and sticky, only to be met by an angry Kevin shouting:

"Where the fuckin' hell, d'ya fink ya goin' slag?"

I was jittery with anxiety but absolutely furious. I was given to understand by Pearl that Kevin was not going to be around, yet here he was, threatening me. In spite of shaking inwardly, I was determined to stand my ground. I slammed the car door shut.

"I was invited here Kevin, get out of my way."

I could see Pearl behind the net curtains of the front room of the unkempt little terraced house with a tangled mess of dried foliage posing as a front garden. Jennie's little head reached just over the windowsill.

I crossed the garden to the window and knocked on the glass.

"Pearl are you staying with this monster, or are you and the children coming with me?"

Kevin stood on the path and I had to swerve around him to reach the window. His body was tense as he visibly seethed with rage.

"She's my fuckin' wife and these are my fuckin' kids and they are staying 'ere."

I hadn't seen Kevin for some years but he looked very changed. He had lost weight and his face was wizened by lines. He was in his mid-thirties but if someone had said he was fifty it would have come as no surprise. His hairline was gradually receding and the youthful attractiveness had all but disappeared. He no longer looked anything like Adam Faith.

He turned around and yelled at me with his face contorted with anger:

"You bleedin' university snobs. You and that Jew bitch. Ya never fort I was good enough for 'er, did yah?"

He continued to rant and rave standing in front of the door barring Pearl's exit and my entrance. At this point the children were crying and screaming. An African-Caribbean woman from the next house came out and waved to me across the dividing low wall of the property:

"Do you want me to call the police, love?"

I yelled at Pearl:

"Make your mind up. .. shall we call the police? How much more are you going to put your kids through Pearl - for this worthless bastard?"

At this point Kevin lost control. He moved swiftly in my direction and struck me full force across the face with such an energy of hatred that I lost my balance and fell backwards striking my head on the neighbours' wall. Blood gushed out of my head as I dazedly grappled a brick to help me get to my feet. Pearl finally managed to force her way out of her front door shouting at Kevin with Dylan screaming hysterically behind her. Kevin made a fast exit into his old, battered van and drove away at speed. Pearl's neighbour rang the police and they arrived within minutes. I made a charge of assault against Kevin and the police then accompanied me to the local hospital as my head was still bleeding profusely and they feared I might need stitches. In fact, I needed four stitches and was very shaken by the experience. But again, compared to my former trauma in Sicily it was nothing more than a minor inconvenience. I kept telling Pearl this as she voiced continuing guilt and remorse over Kevin's behaviour. She told me she had no idea he was going to turn up unexpectedly. It seems he had dropped in to collect some work tools and his intention was not to return to her in spite of his threats to me. Later in the day following my hospital discharge and statement to the police, we were invited around to neighbour Rosie's home for coffee and cakes and Pearl's children played with hers. They had never played together before as Kevin was racist and he hated all 'foreigners' and particularly black people. I stayed the night at Pearl's messy house in Dartford and the next morning Steve came to collect us in his car. I drove slowly behind him from Dartford to Finchley Road with my car full of Pearl's and the children's possessions. I wondered wearily how long it would be before I would be driving everyone and everything back to Dartford again as undoubtedly it would just be a matter of time before Kevin convinced Pearl that he was the real injured party.

With Pearl and family now ensconced at Finchley Road I moved many of my belongings into Steve's flat in West Hampstead. It was at this time I received the telephone call from Anna about her imminent wedding. We made plans to visit Anna's parents in Cardiff in three weeks' time. Anna would take the train to London on Friday afternoon and spend the night with Pearl at the Finchley Road flat. We would then drive to Cardiff from London.

We began our journey from London to Cardiff by earnestly discussing Pearl's situation and wondering whether she would capitulate again and return to Kevin. He hadn't contacted her yet but undoubtedly he would. I eventually managed to change my home telephone number, at great inconvenience, in order to make contact with Pearl difficult. Because Kevin had directly assaulted me, rather than his wife, I was able to take out a legal injunction against him banning him from coming within a five-mile radius of my home. He would no longer be able to sit in his van outside my property and intimidate us all. Paradoxically, his assault on me had turned out to be in everyone's best interest. I said I was surprised that Kevin hated me so much and then I realised that he felt towards Anna and myself how I had felt towards the vice-consul in Catania: the rage against feelings of inferiority perpetuated by the class system. We had all arrogantly believed that Kevin was unaware that we saw him as an uneducated cockney 'bleeder' and not good enough for Pearl. Somehow he had picked up on our mimicry and signals of disdain. He was another man who wasn't stupid either! I was genuinely sorry about our past attitude but Kevin had turned out to be an aggressive and irresponsible husband and father. That was not acceptable in any generation but there was very little we could do about it, only help Pearl to help herself. Anna believed Pearl was suffering from depression and asked me to ensure that she went to see her GP. She also said that the children, Dylan in particular, needed psychological help.

And Anna's situation? It was worse than I thought. Anna had fallen in love with a man she had met at The Council of Christians and Jews. His name was the Rev. Andrew Latimer and he was a Church of England vicar who had completed Theology College some years earlier. Before this he had qualified as a lawyer and worked for a law firm in Nottingham. He was thirty-eight and unmarried. Anna said she loved him very much and wanted to marry him. He was not a rebound love from Yossi. Yossi was now out of her system although she felt she would always love him at a deep emotional level that related to their shared heritage and past together and cherished memories of Israel. She had never met anyone since Yossi's death who came close to triggering such intense feelings of love and compatibility. Andrew felt the same way about her and they both wanted marriage. But what about the Kleins? The Church of England had agreed for Andrew to marry a Jewish wife but they had to be married in church and any children in this instance, because of Andrew's profession, would need to be raised as Christians. In spite of any prospective children's Jewish heritage through the matriarchal line, Anna's children could not be raised as Jews, not even as Liberal Jews. At this point I braked suddenly, almost hitting the car in front of me.

"Hell's bells Anna! You are not going to have me standing by whilst you tell your mother this?"

Ruby Weiz and Joe the Dentist's 'shiksa' were very tame events in comparison. "No", she said. "I just want you to wait outside in the car to give me emotional support when I come out from the house. Andrew wanted to come with me and speak to them but I would not let him. He has no idea what he is up against. For them it is totally unacceptable. I have to make a choice between my parents or my husband to be. I choose Andrew. I will not and cannot ever stop being Jewish - that is part of me. But I will not surrender my happiness to an outdated set of biased patriarchal rules that dictate how I eat, how I dress and who I sleep with. My parents have a choice to cut me off or accept the situation. This time I cannot compromise to please them as I have done so many times in the past".

I was petrified that Dr Klein would have a heart attack at the news or that Juliet would accuse me of having a hand in it. To be fair, in recent years, the Kleins were far more courteous towards me, congratulating me on my job and buying my own flat. They were pleased when I offered accommodation to Anna and just before she left London for Birmingham and they had taken us out for a superb meal at a kosher restaurant in the West End.

We reached the Klein's spacious three-storey residence in a tree-lined avenue of Cardiff. I parked in the street and listened to the car radio whilst Anna was inside discussing her impending marriage with her parents. I had no idea how long she was going to be. After about forty minutes I saw a rabbi arrive in a car. He passed me and swept onto the forecourt at the front of the house. He was in a very great hurry and forgot to lock his car door. He rang the bell and someone let him in. I sunk back into my seat and waited, expecting Anna to be there at least an hour with the rabbi but all of a sudden the door was flung open and Anna ran out followed by the bearded rabbi shouting her name. As I opened my car door I heard the rabbi protest, "Anna, I thought you called me to discuss this matter with yourself. Your parents want..."

"Rabbi Pinkus, I mean no disrespect. I called you to comfort my parents, that is all. I have already made up my mind what I will do and I have no intention of changing it. Good day to you Rabbi. Ah Sian, let's go!"

Pale-faced and determined she hurled herself into the passenger seat and I drove away at speed with Rabbi Pinkus staring open-mouthed behind us.

Anna was married in a 14th century Anglican church in Birmingham. A Liberal rabbi had carried out a special blessing for the couple at the Progressive synagogue in Birmingham the evening before. On the day of the wedding, Anna looked stunning in her stylish white gown with a bodice of tiny seed pearls. Many of her friends attended, and I hugged her with tears of ecstatic joy. It was the first time I had cried since Beni's death. Many of Anna's Jewish friends and work colleagues attended but there was a downside to the day for her: not one member of her own family was there. Andrew's parents came. They lived in Birmingham and it was apparent that they adored Anna and approved of the marriage. Pearl came with her children and we three were briefly reunited again. Sadly, a menacing shadow hung over the wedding because Anna had wanted her parents there. Juliet Klein was adamant that she would not attend the wedding service or reception and insisted that all her family did the same. She argued her points bitterly saying that Anna was denying her religious heritage, culture and grandparents who had died in the Holocaust by marrying a vicar. In the end Dr Klein and Myron attended the blessing at the Progressive Synagogue. Dr Klein met Andrew briefly but could not be persuaded to attend the reception. Anna was very hurt but was determined not to outwardly show her distress. Andrew was well aware of her pain and sadness on her wedding day. He held her hand throughout both ceremonies and gazed directly into her eyes with love and understanding. This was indeed a marriage of true love and compatibility.

Steve and I attended both ceremonies at the church and the synagogue but Steve complained there wasn't much alcohol around at 'Jewish do's' and he said a glass of wine was the best thing to help him relax. Privately, I believed he must mean a bottle. I had never known Steve ever have one glass of wine. But I had to be careful as drinking was a very touchy subject and we ended up arguing if I pursued it. As we rarely argued about other matters, I decided to let the matter rest for the present especially since Steve seemed to be under a fair bit of strain at work. I had mentioned Hal to Steve in passing but downplayed our relationship and never mentioned our meeting in Sardinia. Steve was well aware of my feelings for Beni and the shock of his assassination in front of me. He used to say to me sometimes quite touchingly:

"There's no point trying to compete with a dead man, eh, Sian? They always win as memory erases the bad times and the good times remain as a testimony to a harmonious relationship unachievable with any other human being."

I let him think it was so because it would have meant complex explanations I was not yet ready to disclose to anyone, apart from my psychotherapist. I was now living full time with Steve and the idea of marriage was put to me again on the day of Anna's wedding. I said I would think about it and hated myself for not accepting his proposal as I knew my answer would hurt him. "I'm not ready yet Steve". He would say: 'okay' and kiss me on the cheek as he sipped his wine, "but I can't wait forever for you to get out of those grieving widow's weeds."

We waved off the happy couple to their two-week honeymoon in the Pyrenees. Steve and I together with Pearl and the children had two nights in a hotel in Birmingham. During the second evening at the hotel, Pearl and I consumed almost two bottles of wine with Pearl when ruminating on past times in Foistneth well into the night: Dean falling into the cesspit, Williams Backstreet, Palethorpes' pork pies, Glyn the Gatehouse, and the lads at the Pavilion. We howled with laughter wishing Anna could have joined us but we did not hesitate to vent our spleen on Juliet Klein and her cruel and rejecting behaviour towards her daughter in the name of religion. We avoided the thorny and embarrassing topics of Hal and Kevin but were forced to end our evening abruptly when Dylan interrupted us, crying for Pearl. I immediately left Pearl's room and crept into my own but immediately realised that Steve was missing from the bedroom. I threw some clothes on and rushed downstairs to where I believed him to be. He was indeed there at the bar, glass in hand, chatting to a man and a woman next to him on the high bar stools. I went back to bed fearing the worst. I believed Steve was fast becoming an alcoholic and I was becoming more and more disappointed and unsettled within our relationship.

Kevin contacted Pearl again by letter after three months of no contact. It was apparent that the woman he had left Pearl for had ditched him and he was back on the scene trying to disrupt Pearl and his children's lives. But this time Pearl held firm. She had already filed for divorce on grounds of adultery and physical abuse. As the children were known to Social Services who would testify against Kevin, this made Pearl's case for divorce more substantial. She hoped that this way she would be rid of Kevin more quickly. She continued to live at the Finchley Road flat and pay the bills. I refused to charge rent as the children were badly in need of clothes and Kevin avoided maintenance payments. Pearl's sole income was now state benefits. When Steve lamented that I should charge something in addition to the bills, I pointed out that we spent more money on alcohol and smoking in a week than Pearl did on feeding and clothing her family. Steve did not raise the topic again. When she became more settled, with Jennie attending the local primary school, Pearl took a refresher course in shorthand typing and within six months was working as a part-time temp in a local office, almost within walking distance of the flat. Slowly and gradually, her life and the lives of her children began to improve. In just under two years, she received her Decree Absolute from the Divorce Registry. Her marriage to Kevin was well and truly over.

Chapter 19

Music 'Walk of Life', Dire Straits (1985)

Pearl applied to Camden Council for a council property as she was virtually homeless and I put the case to Camden that I needed my own flat back. We combined our efforts with the housing department and within eight months Pearl was allocated a well allocated and spacious two storey house in Gospel Oak, near Hampstead Heath and within walking distance of The Royal Free Hospital and a ten-minute journey by car from my flat out of peak times. It was when Pearl was visiting the casualty department of the hospital with Jennie who had fallen off a swing, that she met Enid Morgan, the little girl at the Foistneth Fair who had been raped by her uncle. Enid was working as a nurse at the Royal Free Hospital. Pearl invited Enid over to her house and they struck up a friendship that lasted many years. Pearl had few friends outside of myself and Anna but Anna now lived permanently in Birmingham. Pearl was fortunate enough to find an administrative job working for Camden Council. It was at a local project for homeless women in abusive relationships. She had been sent on various courses relating to her work and was toying with the idea of training as a social worker. The children had been taken off the 'at risk' register with Social Services and both Dylan and Jennie thrived without Kevin around. Dylan began to develop confidence and Jennie's behavioural problems ceased. I used to baby-sit for Pearl sometimes at weekends. Steve liked this as it involved us sitting in with bottles of wine. Sometimes he would sneak off to his favourite pub in Hampstead and I wouldn't see him till closing time. I rang Alcoholics Anonymous but they told me Steve would have to make contact himself if he wanted help. This he would never do as in spite of being a psychologist he believed he did not have an alcohol problem. A.A. helpfully suggested I attend 'Al Anon', an organisation that supports relatives of dependent drinkers. After my first Al Anon meeting, I knew Steve had a problem. Before then I experienced doubt because he was able to carry out a competent job as a clinical psychologist working with the elderly in the NHS. He never drank in the morning and he never drank at work. He rarely drove a car when inebriated and there were days when he did not touch alcohol at all, although these had become far fewer of late. Remembering how bad my mother was with 'the shakes' in the morning, I often felt I was wrong about Steve being an alcoholic. I believed him when he said he could 'take alcohol or leave it.' But after my Al Anon meetings, I began to question why he didn't leave it. Steve was a different kind of drinker to my mother but it didn't make him less dependent. Moreover, any mention of alcohol made Steve angry in a way that nothing else did. I tried to hold my tongue but found it difficult at times, especially when I stumbled across a stack of empty bottles hidden carefully away in places where he believed I wouldn't look.

The Finchley Road flat was empty again. I had experienced two sets of short-term tenants from overseas after Pearl and family had vacated the flat. I then decided to re-decorate it as I has an urge to move back into my own accommodation. I needed space from Steve. He was talking marriage again and one night in early November, I casually agreed to marry him sometime at the end of the decade. I regretted it the next day but felt guilty about telling him so. I was now thirty-five and felt an old maid as I had never been married and all my friends either were or had been. I thought it unlikely I would meet anyone else as I lived with Steve, we both were faithful to one another and we had an enviable compatibility that made our relationship survive. Then I started to have dreams about Hal. I dreamed I was lying in his arms and waking up to the sheer pleasure of kissing him on the lips and feeling his body next to mine. Once I found myself kissing Steve on the lips, but when I had blundered out of sleep long enough to recognise who it was, I experienced overwhelming loss and frustration. Once I woke up sobbing when I dreamed Hal and I were on a boat together but the boat capsized and Hal had drowned. I couldn't stand the dreams any longer and in early December I decided to ring Hal's office to check if he was all right. I made myself believe that my intention was only that, nothing more. But he had left his previous job and took some tracking down. When I finally found the telephone number of his office in the city, I was put straight through to Hal without going via his secretary.

"Sian?", the familiar voice said. "Is that really you? Are you still in Italy?" 'Cold, slightly imperious', I thought.

"I live in London, Hal. I didn't marry Beni. He died."

Silence.

"Are you married?"

"No. I live with someone."

"I have re-married. I left Julia as you know. My wife is called Lynne and we have a six-year-old daughter".

I knew then that I had made a terrible mistake in calling him. I felt cold all over and gutted, abandoned, disappointed and God knows what else. I just needed to get off the phone and think. But he wasn't going to let me go that easily.

"Why did you phone Sian?"

"Because I dreamed you were dead. I wanted – tears began to run down my face, "to see if you were okay…"

"I want to see you again", he said in a kindlier tone. "Why don't you and your partner come down to Chichester for New Year's Eve. We are having some friends down for the weekend but we are not doing anything spectacular. Lynne will do a meal for us all and we can welcome in the new decade at our local."

'At least Steve will appreciate that', I thought wryly. Was this how it was to end then? The ex-passionate lovers now friends complete with partners, spending a congenial weekend in Kent with appropriate green wellies, corny conversation that passes for intellectual debate, and with the recommended tipple at the atmospheric 'Olde Worlde' pub. I agreed it was a good plan but in my heart I knew I did not want to go. Nevertheless, I was unable to refuse for some unknown reason, maybe curiosity about his new wife or something more significant buried deep down in my psyche. I greatly regretted telephoning Hal.

Steve was keen to go to Chichester as we were not doing anything exciting over the New Year. Anna was pregnant with her second child and did not intend travelling from Birmingham. Pearl had promised to take her children to Foistneth for Christmas and they were all staying with Brenda the Boast. Most of our preferred acquaintances were not spending the Christmas holidays in London so we both felt we needed some social activity over the holiday period. We decided we'd only have one night over with the Stanton's and we arrived in Chichester at 2 p.m. of the afternoon of the 31st December. It was a bright morning in central London but it had grown damp and overcast as we reached the Kent coast. Hal's house was near the sea in a place called Bracklesham Bay. It was a large white detached 1930s property with a long sweep of a drive. "Very nice", Steve commented on arrival, "this friend of yours has a bob or two". We were met by Hal, his wife and a red setter called Bernie. Bernie leapt at the car excitedly and Hal called him to heel. I hugged Hal and his wife enthusiastically as if we had all been old friends all our lives. I introduced them to Steve and Lynne took us to our rooms. As we entered the front porch a little girl ran out. She was aged about six and had dark hair cut in a bob. Lynn stopped and said to the child:

"Say hello Sian, this is Auntie Sian and Uncle … eh Steve."

I looked at Lynne in utter amazement. "Your daughter is called Sian? What an unusual choice. Do you have Welsh blood?"

"No, Hal liked the name. He told me you did some temping for him when you were a student. Oh, this is your room. Hang onto the windows if you open them. This room is facing the sea and the force of the wind is so great that they swing right back on their hinges and are almost impossible to close. This is the en-suite and the towels are here." Lynne chatted away whilst Steve commented on 'my temping.' He said cynically that Hal must have been a very patient boss because it took me three hours of laboriously striking keys on a typewriter to produce anything approximating to a letter. I found being at Hal's an uncomfortable experience and instantly regretted coming. Hal looked more or less the same, but older with a smattering of grey at the temples, that made him look distinguished. I felt the surge of my old feelings towards him but was both frustrated and irritated because I wanted to feel nothing other than the good will of friendship. I felt anger towards this man who had featured so prominently in my life and had brought me nothing but pain and disappointment. But I was determined to override all negative feelings and make the best of the weekend.

Hal's wife was much younger than me. I guessed about mid-twenties. She came from a monied family and was very keen on horses. I smugly noticed that she was not as slim as me and that although she had a pleasant face and warm personality, she was unglamorous and certainly not beautiful. Sian was delightful and was fascinated by the fact that we both had the same name. She wanted to sit by me and told me enthusiastically about her new school. Steve had found Hal's drinks cabinet and was already enjoying a single malt whiskey. I had a coffee as I felt I had had enough alcohol over Christmas with Steve to last me well into the millennium. The other guests were Hal's friends, John and Fi, then there was Grace, Lynne's divorcee mother and current babysitter. Their other friends and neighbours would join us at the pub later. About 3 p.m., Lynn suggested that the guests all stroll along to the local for an hour or two and then return, have a shower and prepare for dinner. The landlord knew everyone in the area and had extended his drinking times to 'open all day' in a function room at the back of the pub to outwit the licensing laws. Lynne also ventured that she had some preparations to do for the evening meal and turned down offers of assistance from Fi and myself. She was keen for her mother (Grace) to go to the pub as she would be 'Sian sitting' when we all went out after dinner. Our small group was veering towards the back exit door complete with anoraks and outdoor shoes when Hal suddenly said he would take the dog for a brief walk. He openly asked me to accompany him.

"The others have all done this once today. You could do with a walk after your trip from London. We'll only be half an hour and we'll join you all at the pub. Coming Steve?"

Steve refused as he could literally smell the real ale. I have often idly wondered how things would have developed if Steve had accepted Hal's invitation to join us for a walk that afternoon.

We walked along a flat and muddy path running parallel to the road. It dipped suddenly and the road disappeared from view. From here we could see the grey shoreline in the rapidly falling dusk of early evening and hear the persistent splash of the water against a small wooden jetty.

"Not quite Sardinia, is it?", said Hal. He stopped and let Bernie off the lead. The dog immediately sprinted in the direction of the jetty, sniffing at plants enthusiastically and lifting his back leg along the way.

I said nothing. I did not know what to say.

"Why Sian? I want to know why you ended it?"

"You soon consoled yourself with another woman. How old is your daughter, six? We last saw each other eight years ago. You didn't lose any time getting another woman into your bed after your split from Julia."

"Before actually. What does it matter to you? You left me."

"I had to Hal. I had no choice. I couldn't live with myself after all that happened on my return to Sicily from Sardinia."

I told him everything as we walked along the shore, about Beni's assassination, my nights in prison and Lord T's telephone call. He interrupted me at this point saying quickly that he had been called into the office by the Project Head some weeks after his return and had been told that Lord T had rung asking about him and about some incident at the villa. Hal had assumed we had damaged something and asked for clarification, saying he would ring Lord T if necessary. Lord T never contacted again and Hal forgot the episode, until now. He went on to say that when he received my letter he had felt hurt and very angry with me. He then met Lynne who reminded him a little of me in character.

"She was outspoken, rather sassy for such a young girl."

He had met her at her father's riding stables in Tunbridge Wells where his children were having riding lessons. He soon became attracted to her. He said in retrospect, he probably wanted to get out of his marriage to Julia and he also wanted to heal the wounds from our passionate but irreparable relationship. He convinced himself he was in love with Lynne but he soon discovered that he was not. Lynne became pregnant and wanted to have an abortion. He was against it and made the decision there and then to leave Julia.

"Sian is a beautiful child", he said. He said he was very attached to her which makes their marriage bearable. How ironic, how very, very ironic. He marries a girl he doesn't love to stop her having an abortion and he calls the baby 'Sian'. Our lives were unfolding more and more in the vein of a black comedy and I wondered whether I should consider sending the script to Woody Allen.

As we walked and talked, Hal put his arms around my shoulders in his old unique way. He gazed across the grey skyline with its fast-failing light, interrupting his reverie only to toss an occasional stick to Bernie.

Suddenly he looked into my eyes, "You protected me, didn't you? How much you loved me, Sian. I'm not worth it, you know."

"I know that", I said and surprisingly meant it.

"You still love me, don't you?"

"Hal, stop it. We must go back now."

I wrenched myself away from his grasp but he pulled me towards him again and kissed me full on the lips. I found my mouth opening to receive his tongue and then felt his hands moving up inside my ski jacket and under my thick woollen jumper. I felt his hands caress my breasts and he whispered into my neck:

"You are the only woman I know whose nipples are aroused the moment they are touched. I felt his hand skate gently across my bare skin as he touched the waistband of my trousers and fumbled with the zip. I felt his hand slip inside my panties.

"No. Damn you Hal!", I shouted. "This I won't do, let me go. Stop now!"

He held me.

"Sian, darling I love you. I have loved you for so many years and I felt so angry at being rejected by you. I thought you had dumped me deliberately to get even after the way I had treated you in the past. What would you have thought if you had received a letter like the one you sent to me? I know I am an insensitive bastard but I'm trying to change. Please, darling. This may be our last time together."

He pulled me off the path and into the direction of a tree which screened any passers-by from view. He took off his jacket and laid it on the floor under the tree. He pushed me gently down onto it.

"Hal, people could go past… they…"

"It's highly unlikely here in the dark at Bracklesham Bay on New Year's Eve".

He penetrated me and I responded with a scream of pleasure causing Bernie to bark and rush up to us. Hal yelled "go away Bernie," and had to pull out of me and throw him a stick. I hadn't realised how long it had been since I had sex, enjoyed real sex, like this. He murmured "you are so moist darling, hold me inside. Oh, this is so pleasurable. Relax my love, no one will come past. Sian, forget the dog, he's okay."

I think Bernie interrupted us once more but by then I was well away into the beginning of orgasm. In all these years, this was how I remembered sex with Hal. I had always harboured forbidden thoughts of our lovemaking. This was how it should be because we were so attuned to each other's bodies even after years of no contact. We reached orgasm and our cries of uninhibited delight mingled with the screams of the gulls flying across the estuary of Bracklesham Bay.

Lynne had prepared a substantial meal and that evening we ate at their large oval table in the dining-room. Later we would all go to the pub to celebrate the arrival of the New Year. Steve and I were seated at the opposite end of the table to Hal and Lynne. I got up at one point to fetch the cauliflower bake as everyone was so engrossed in their conversations that they did not hear my repeated request. I got to Hal's elbow and he turned to me and smiled; as he passed the dish his hand ever so briefly touched mine. It was such a fast caress, no one could possibly be aware of it. But unbeknown to me, Steve had seen the gesture and noted it. At the countdown to midnight in the pub, I had somehow managed to get myself wedged between Hal and Fi. Lynn was behind talking to John and Steve. When the clock finally struck the last chime of midnight, everyone shouted 'Happy New Year!' Hal bent down and kissed me fully on the lips "Happy New Year, Sian!" He then tactfully moved in the direction of his wife for the next embrace. Steve appeared at my elbow. His eyes were glazed from drink and he was glowering:

"Don't you think you should kiss your own partner first before kissing someone else's?"

I laughed off his remark but felt very awkward. Steve was undeniably drunk again and I feared he would make a scene. Fortunately, he did not but I was very relieved when we got back to the house and he fell asleep fully clothed on top of the bedcover. I refused to think too much about what had happened that day. After tossing and turning for a short while, the distant sound of the sea lulled me into a deep but troubled sleep.

The next day we said our goodbyes and drove back to London before lunch on the pretext of my having some work to complete. I drove and Steve sat morosely in the car and said little all the way back to North London. I thought about Hal and myself and how on the previous day after making love on the footpath, I had told Hal, "only contact me if you are free from commitments to any other woman." I stated categorically that I would not contact him ever again. I meant it. I had handed over our love for one another to God or fate. I would initiate no action this time. There was also the problem of Steve; I knew I could no longer continue in our relationship but I felt guilty as I knew he had more feelings for me than I had for him.

I went into the kitchen of the West Hampstead flat and aimed for the fridge wondering if we could put together some of our remaining food for lunch. I was very hungry as we had only had toast early morning, refusing the offer of a cooked breakfast in our hurry to get away. Steve came out of the living-room with a glass of red wine in his hand. I looked at him in amazement.

"Steve, you are not going to start drinking **now** on an empty stomach."

He glared across the table at me in silence and then said:

"What a two-timing, hypocritical little bitch you are."

I stopped in front of the fridge, frozen to the spot.

"And I bought into it - me a psychologist! I bought the bereavement and the post-traumatic stress and the horrendous trauma of seeing your loved one's head blown off. And I believed in time you would get over the shock of dear Beni's death and you might even be happy with another man. 'Dear Beni' may eventually have come down a notch or two from that pedestal where you so carefully placed him for my benefit and the world's benefit. Instead, dear old Beni is nothing more than a myth and you were fucking this guy! You told me he was an old friend and it was long over. Like hell! Do you think no one noticed the way you two looked at each other? I could have accepted the fucking, maybe ... but not this. Why Sian, why did you lie about him?"

I sighed, realising I could not spare his feelings.

"I didn't lie", I said. "I stretched the truth a bit. I have loved Hal Stanton for almost twenty years. I went to Chichester hoping I was over it. Sadly, it can never be over."

I leaned against the fridge. I had a splitting headache and desperately wanted to get away. Steve lost his temper and threw his wine glass down hard hitting the side of the kitchen table. The glass shattered but one of the shards bounced upwards and caught me on the face just below my left eye. The blood spurted out of my face and I felt as if I was fainting. I could hear Steve calling "Sian, darling no, hang on, sit down. Sit down now, I'll call an ambulance". He ran to the bathroom and got a towel which I held to my face. At this point I feared I would lose an eye and I kept hysterically screaming for him to ring an ambulance. It was New Year's Day so there was only a skeleton service but the ambulance did arrive almost an hour later. By this time, we were heading for the car, with me clutching a towel to my face.

I was admitted to hospital and had to stay overnight because the consultant ophthalmologist was unavailable until the next morning. Steve went back to get my night things in a state of panic and guilt. Unbeknown to me at that time, Steve phoned Anna who told him the whole story of Hal and myself and how she doubted whether I would ever be able to shake off my obsession with Hal. She also advised him to let me go as we were making each other miserable. She was right as indifference and addiction is what we had drifted into after five years of our intimate relationship. On a lighter note, my left eye was not damaged as the shard of glass had fortunately missed my eye but opened a blood vessel in my cheek. The glass was removed by a senior nurse followed by two stitches. I was told there should only be light scarring. On the second of January I returned to my own flat in Finchley Road and Steve and I agreed to separate. He did attempt to re-kindle our relationship some weeks later with multiple apologies but I was adamant I would not continue to live a lie. I was on my own again and I believed it was likely to be that way for a very long time.

It was one Saturday in mid-June when the weather turned scorching for a few freak days causing chaos on the overcrowded tubes in central London. The city bars and pubs were full of irate foreign tourists lamenting on the inability of the British to serve alcoholic drinks below room temperature. I was at home that weekend, ironing some of my summer dresses and listening to the radio when the telephone rang. It was Hal. Hearing his voice shocked me and I feared the worst - he was dying or some dreadful accident had happened. It turned out Lynne had left him for another man and she had taken Sian with her. I couldn't make sense of it at first. Women did not leave Hal Stanton; he left them. But Lynne had done the unthinkable and found a younger man who was a keen horseman and as mad about horses as Lynne herself was. Hal said that she had been having an affair for about a year so she wasn't too bothered by our behaviour in Chichester. Like Steve, she too had picked up the vibes between us. But Hal missed Sian and felt disconcerted by the sudden changes to his lifestyle. His whole world had been turned upside down. He was living in the Chichester house with the dog until it was finally sold. Lynne had moved in with her lover and had instigated divorce proceedings on the grounds of 'irreconcilable differences.' She was entitled to half the proceeds from the family home. His other beautiful home in Watford had been given to Julia in the divorce settlement. He was maintaining three children and for the moment, two ex-wives. Hal was strapped for cash, a very new experience for him as he had always benefited from a comfortable income.

Hal seemed quite flat in mood when he asked about Steve. I told him that our relationship ended after Chichester and he seemed relieved. I suggested he came over that same evening if he was free (it wouldn't have surprised me if he had not already found some woman somewhere) and I would cook us a meal at the flat. He arrived just after seven and I had made a rich lasagne with mixed salad and a fruit compote with fresh cream. Hal complained about not finding a place to park near the flat and he seemed to have lost a lot of his old sparkle. He had also lost a lot of weight and his face looked quite thin. Hal liked the flat and said that although it was small, it was sunny and well-appointed and conveniently close to the tube station. He complimented me on my good taste in furnishings. We talked about the present and avoided mentioning the past. When it got to ten o'clock, Hal mumbled something about returning home. I looked at him in amazement.

"You are not going to drive back to Chichester tonight, darling. Tell me, what is it?"

He paced the room and then sat down on the sofa his face in his hands.

"Hal, I've never known you like this. In the usual circumstances, you and I would have been in the bedroom two hours ago. Is this about the lack of excitement because we are legitimately here, with no one to cheat on and no tantalising excitement of voyeurism from passing strangers? Was our relationship so without substance that the only thing maintaining it was the cheap thrills of sexual risk?"

"I can't do it Sian, I can't. I feel I don't have anything left. I feel energy-less, drained. I don't have motivation for anything. Lynne left in February but I didn't contact you because there were so many things to do and sort out. I thought it would be unfair to dump my problems on you. I shouldn't have come here today as I am still not coping well."

I dropped down on my knees in front of him as he sat on the sofa. I kissed his bowed head and spoke to him lovingly and firmly:

"Darling, I love you so much. Do you really think I care whether or not you can get an erection tonight? Knowing you, it won't be long before that happens. Hal darling, please don't upset yourself, you are not in a good mental or physical state. Please darling, let's go to bed and just lie next to each other tonight. I need to hold you and tell you how happy and content I am to have you here with me. Hal, please don't get upset. I love you so much, it really is of no importance......"

We eventually went to bed together, kissing tenderly and holding each other close. Eventually sleep overwhelmed us and we cuddled up together, Hal's hand in mine, just like an old married couple.

Chapter 20

Music: *'Sweet Dreams' (Are Made of This)*, The Eurythmics (1983)

Hal and I were married at Camden Registry Office at King's Cross in May of 1985. Anna and Pearl were at the wedding, complete with children and partners. Pearl was dating a senior social worker called Paul Edgcombe. She was still involved in running the project for single mothers in Kentish Town but she was also studying two days a week for qualifications in social work. Pearl felt it was a stable period in her life and she said she was as happy now as she had been in the long-forgotten Oxfordshire days with the Mellor-Clarkes. She felt her life had a meaning and purpose and she was committed to her work. Dylan was still a socially withdrawn boy at nearly fifteen but he had managed to make an odd friend here and there and was achieving good grades in his favourite subjects at school. Jennie was very bright and had adjusted well to her school after Pearl's split from Kevin. They were still living in council accommodation but in a quiet street composed of private residences. Paul was a couple of years or so older than Pearl and still single, although he had had a long-term relationship with a nurse some years before meeting her.

Anna and Andrew brought their two handsome and very lively sons to the wedding. They were called Daniel and Ben, aged 6 and 3 respectively. Andrew was a devoted father, actively involved in his children's care. He even changed Ben's nappy during the reception meal at a local hotel in St. John's Wood, within a short bus ride from the clandestine Baker Street flat of many years earlier. This new approach to parenting was all too much for Hal who was a million light years away from 'new age dad' but he liked and approved of both Paul and Andrew. We had invited mutual friends and acquaintances to our reception party. Unexpectedly, Hal's 21-year-old son Alex showed up. He was meant to graduate the following month but Julia continuously lamented that he was lazy and not applying himself to his studies. She was vehemently against his attending our wedding but Alex had ignored her venomous outpourings. Alex had inherited Hal's hair colouring and beautiful blue eyes. He resembled his father a little in profile but Hal said that overall, he physically resembled his mother far more than him. Julia was furious that Hal had married again (it was rumoured that she hoped to get him back after his split from Lynne) and when I featured in her conversation I was described as 'the Welsh trollop' to her children and friends. Hal's daughter Elizabeth would have nothing to do with her father from the time he left the family home. He had tried to arrange parental visits but only Alex was prepared to spend time with his father. Elizabeth totally ignored him even when he sent her birthday cards and gifts. We both knew that this was Julia's 'poisonous indoctrination' of the children from an early age. I used to tell him this again and again in order to reassure him and lessen his distress as he was deeply hurt by his daughter's behaviour. On the other hand, 10-year-old Sian spent a lot of time with us as Lynne had a very different attitude to Hal and myself. Lynne and I occasionally spoke to each other on the telephone regarding Sian's needs and travel arrangements. We now called Sian, 'Shanna' (Beni's old name for me) to distinguish her name from mine. She looked so beautiful on our wedding day in her yellow taffeta dress, her dark hair swept up in a fashionable coil on top of her head under a small garland of blue and yellow flowers. She loved playing with Jennie and the other children there. Everyone said I looked radiant in my cream, plunge-line wedding dress and plumed headdress, in the style of the 1930s. We had arranged it so that we would have a honeymoon in June when both of us were free. Anna, Andrew and their children stayed with us on the wedding night whilst Shanna stayed with Jennie. In the end Alex decided to stay with a friend in another part of London as there were "too many brats around" for his liking.

Hal and I had disposed of our respective homes. His house in Chichester was finally sold the September after we got together permanently. He reluctantly moved into my Finchley Road flat saying it was too small. He had a lot of furniture and equipment left over from the Chichester House which he was forced to put into storage. We stayed in the flat seven months before I finally found a buyer. Together we bought a splendid, roomy three bedroom and two-bathroom leasehold flat in Eton Avenue, Swiss Cottage. We made a legal agreement stating that whichever one of us lived the longer could stay in the flat for their lifetime. On the death of both partners, the flat would be divided between Shanna, Jennie and Dylan. Hal's other children would inherit the Watford house he had bought for Julia. It seemed a fair deal and we were both happy with it. Over the past months Hal's physical health had greatly improved and he was very much his old self on the day of the wedding.

At the reception party, Alex had a little too much to drink. He wittily revived his favourite topic, the six wives of King Henry VIII, a king also known by the nickname 'Bluff King Hal'. After the photographs at the wedding reception, and following both a touching and amusing reminiscence toast given by Andrew, Alex shouted across the table to Shanna:

"Get thee in the photo young miss, for you are the daughter of that strumpet, Anne Boleyn and our future Queen of England. "And madam", he said to Jennie, "Grow up quickly for methinks you will be wife number four when Good Queen Sian turns up her toes. But remember, you may lose your head!"

This made the young contingent giggle and chase around the room in fits of laughter. Memories were evoked as I reflected on the silliness of our own youth when Pearl, Anna and myself, would imitate Theodore's monotone about Cliff Bayley selling our marbles for gambling and 'Glyn the Gatehouse's fondness for the word 'lovely'. We would giggle non-stop, to the exasperation of any adult still sober but here it was different. Hal was plainly embarrassed by the references to his many marriages and irritated by his son's antics but I insisted that he let the matter drop.

'Kevin the Bleeder' surfaced about eighteen months after Pearl had left him and he demanded to see 'his' children. The partner he had been living with had thrown him out. Failing to re-gain admittance to her council flat, he tried Pearl again, insisting on having access to the children. Dylan refused to have anything to do with him but he managed to take Jennie to McDonald's twice in North London before becoming bored with the whole thing and disappearing again as Pearl predicted he would. Sometime later Paul moved into the house with her and the children and together they purchased their property from Camden Council under 'the right to buy' act introduced by the then

Prime Minister, Margaret Thatcher.

On the day of my wedding, I was serenely happy. I had all my dearest friends present and I felt really blessed. Even in my wildest dreams, I could never imagine myself married to Hal. Here I was with his children at our wedding, which also included my two dearest friends and their families. My mother had been invited and she was positive about Hal (at least to his face) but did not attend as she said it was 'too much' for her. In vain we offered to fetch her by car but she found all the excuses in the world. I was not hurt because I had been in therapy long enough to have learned not to have any expectations of my mother. On this perfect day, there was part of me that feared things were going too well and I did not deserve them. I anticipated the cutting blow of fate.

Nothing happened and our lives seemed to sail gently along into smooth but uncharted waters.

Chapter 21

Music: *'Everybody Hurts',* R.E.M. (1992)

Over the ensuing years, there were some minor difficulties within our marriage. Hal did not want to continue living at the flat in Swiss Cottage but wanted us to move to Surrey or Sussex and commute into town to work. As his company was situated in Canary Wharf and I worked in Holborn, it seemed absurd why we should move out of town and be reliant on the crowded, dirty and erratic trains of Network Southeast. I had never been a Home Counties commuter and I loathed the idea. The only real home I had known was Northwest London and I did not want to leave it until I retired. I had built up a network of friends and work colleagues and I insisted that the last thing I wanted was an 'over-priced mock Tudor box' in Tunbridge Wells. I said that I was a city career girl, not a county housewife as his other wives had been and that I loved my airy, spacious flat at Swiss Cottage. Its most outstanding feature was the delicate stained-glass window halfway up the flight of stairs leading to top floor and also the huge, light living room with decorative plasterwork on the ceiling, opening onto a wrought-iron balcony overlooking the communal garden. There were two flats in the converted house, ours was comprised of the first and second floors and the other was the basement maisonette. "I miss watering the garden", lamented Hal, adding this to his latest list of moans about inner city life.

"Well, you'll have to water the geraniums in the window box", I said, irritably, "Also we have Hampstead Heath, Primrose Hill and Regent's Park within walking distance. There is plenty of countryside and greenery that we are not required to tend to or spend money on. Hal, I will not move from here. If you go, you go alone." Hal also missed his red setter Bernie, that had to be restored to Lynne as my Finchley Road flat was an unsuitable place for dogs.

Because Hal had always been the main salary earner and his ex-wives had been housewives, he tended to take me for granted and assumed I would do the domestics without his participation. This was unacceptable in the 1980s so I insisted he took his part in shopping and cooking especially when his children were staying. I always took care of the washing and ironing. I had a cleaner once a week, the flat being time-consuming for me to clean and keep organised without help. I was drawn to thinking of my childhood heroines in my favourite novels. Those novels ended at the churchyard for either weddings or funerals. Just as well. I could not conceive of Elizabeth Bennett saying to the enigmatic Darcy in Pride and Prejudice:

"Mr Darcy, why do you always forget to put petrol in the Range Rover? It's so unfair, when I go out, there's hardly enough in it to crawl to the edge of Pemberley. I spent an age filling it up last week!" Or Cathy to Heathcliff in Wuthering Heights: "Oh stop moaning, Heathcliff! How is it that every time we are due to go to Edgar's you always complain that your favourite shirt is either in the dirty linen basket or un-ironed." No, better to end it at the church and let the reader imagine their future love life of perfect bliss uncluttered by the dreary practicalities of modern living.

Our sex life continued unabated and what we lost on the domestics we made up for in bed. Hal and I made love most of the time with the same passion for each other and with imagination and creativity. But these days we kept our lovemaking to the rooms of our home. Fortunately, there was no flat directly below us as there had been in Finchley Road so we could make love on either the floor or the bed without reverberation causing concern to the neighbours directly below.

There were times when I was unable to relax because I feared Hal would be unfaithful to me as he had been to all the other women he had been involved with. Possessively, I watched for all the signs acknowledging I was making myself deliberately miserable as there was no evidence he was unfaithful. When I watched my friends and acquaintances interact with Hal, any harmless flirtation would drive me into a frenzy of jealousy. So, I went back into therapy with my psychotherapist in Hampstead. She told me I lacked a positive father figure and I was always 'pleasing daddy' by pleasing Hal. When I refused him anything I felt guilty and felt afraid he would abandon me as my father had done. I once reflected after a therapy session: "this is a load of very expensive baloney. The real reason why I fear Hal's infidelity is because he has spent his life being unfaithful to every damn woman he's had a relationship with, whether he loved her or not."

He told me himself that he had had affairs with Julia's married friends. He had had one-night stands and affairs of longer duration. He was still seeing some woman or other when we were together at the Baker Street flat. One of Julia's married friends had told Julia about her affair with Hal. The friend then overdosed with tablets and spent the night having her stomach pumped out in hospital. Hal denied the affair but Julia never trusted him again. It was not surprising that she was so bitter and vindictive towards him.

I continued my Al Anon meetings and also went to a group called 'Adult Children of Alcoholics' where I shared my inability to '*let go and let God*. I learnt I must trust a Higher Power that will ensure everything will work out for the best. I must let go of my control over people, places and things. I must let Hal free and trust the process. He had disclosed to me once using a more solemn tone than usual:

"I have slept with many women Sian, but you are the only woman I have really loved. I know you love me for who I am, not for who or what you want me to be."

This triggered my on-going curiosity about his past because I had never asked him much about his background. I had always feared to raise questions about his past should my curiosity make him feel ill at ease or even angry. In the thorny centre of this historic tale was his past marriage to Julia.

Hal was born in Seven Oaks in Kent, an only child. His father was a surveyor by profession and his mother owned and ran a very large and successful florist shop. Hal was a bright boy and went to the Grammar School and then to St Andrews University to study civil engineering. His mother adored him; nothing was too good for her bright, good-looking son and when he married Julia Carlton-Webb, the niece of the managing director and major shareholder of the first company he worked for after graduation, his mother expected no less. Privately the Carlton-Webbs thought that Julia, with her private education and finishing school in Switzerland, could have done much better for herself. But Hal had potential and Julia was determined to have him. Julia's expectations were that Hal would grow tired of civil engineering and aim for a high-flying business career in real estate, the city or politics. But Hal liked what he was doing, building bridges and high-rise blocks of offices. He enjoyed golf, football and of course, women in his free time. He did not have the stomach for Machiavellian politics or enough dedication to a belief or cause to motivate him to pursue a specific ambition outside of his work. Julia loved Hal in spite of her dissatisfaction with his choice of career, at but when her trust was betrayed she totally changed. She became resentful and vitriolic and turned against him. Julia was determined Hal's children would not forgive him either for his actions towards them and his ultimate abandonment.

Hal's father died the year after his marriage to Julia and he lost his mother to heart disease when I was living in Italy. He found the death of his mother extremely painful, but he had spoken of it to me a couple of times in a heart-rending way. I could deeply relate to grief and loss as I still mourned for my grandmother, the linchpin of my childhood.

Lynne, on the other hand, had chosen her horses and country lifestyle over Hal and there was also a considerable age gap between them. Their encounter had taken place against the backdrop of tragic circumstances surrounding our relationship. It had been a costly mistake. When Hal left Julia for Lynne, Julia had twice attempted suicide and Hal had almost returned to her out of fear and compassion. I became aware that if our relationship had gone ahead when it was meant to, I could never have lived with the guilt of hurting Julia. I do believe things happen for a reason even if the reason is unclear to us at the time. I was compensated for not having children by my relationship with Shanna who was very precious to me. It was like a mother-daughter relationship but without the mutual baggage of emotional demands. Shanna gave us both so much pleasure. She spent two weekends in four with us and a large chunk of every vacation. We took her with us to Italy, France and Turkey. She loved swimming and was unaffected by severe heat. Shanna was not horsy in spite of her mother's best efforts to encourage her to ride. She preferred to draw horses rather than sit astride them and she preferred the dusty streets of Camden to the leafy lanes of Kent. She had her father's aptitude for mathematics, particularly geometry, and her mother's friendliness and social ease. Lynne was not possessive of her daughter and when she became pregnant again by her new husband, 'Jerome Forster-Jones, the horse-trainer', I was secretly pleased as I thought we would have a new role in Shanna's life, providing her with the security of our undivided love and attention. At home Shanna would need to share her mother with her stepfather and new half-sibling. Rather surprisingly it did not appear to bother her at all.

Hal was settling into our routine at Swiss Cottage although he continued to complain about the lack of space and the disadvantages of living in a flat without a garden. In time he agreed it was a good thing to be free of tending plants and lawns. Living in central London meant we had easy access to the theatres and art galleries and the advantage of always finding a black cab prepared to go to Swiss Cottage from the West End. Pearl had found this a nightmare when she was living in Forest Hill, as most cabbies had an aversion to driving south of the river in the evening unless they lived there. Hal used the smallest of our three bedrooms as an office and his desk contained charts and an interesting array of geometrical instruments used by civil engineers. He worked the odd day from home which helped his stress levels. He had also taken up jogging on Primrose Hill and he mentioned to me how he loved to have a short break at the top of the hill and focus on the spectacular view of London, whilst identifying the distant famous landmarks across the sweep of the River Thames from the Post Office Tower to Canary Wharf. On a clear day you could see Battersea Power Station to the West of the horizon and the dome of St. Paul's to the East. In spite of angrily complaining about the dog mess on his trainers, Hal became less critical and more attached to his immediate surroundings. I was relieved he had given up the idea of 'the detached residence with mature garden' in Surrey.

I had begun to attend the Liberal synagogue again in the area. I felt I needed to develop more of a spiritual basis to my life and the only time I had got minimally close to this was when I had attended the Liberal synagogue with Anna some years ago. I thought seriously about it and decided I would convert to Judaism, an arduous business that takes years and is not encouraged within the faith. However, converts are accepted ('Jews by Choice') and made welcome once they have made a serious religious commitment to Judaism. Hal agreed in principle so long as he did not have to convert. He said he was prepared to come along to some of the social activities at the synagogue but said he wished I had taken up yoga instead. When he discovered that the bacon, pork chops and seafood had disappeared from the house he became annoyed. Over the period of Passover when it was forbidden to eat bread or anything containing leaven for eight days, he learned that the practice of Judaism was going to directly affect him. We had quite a number of Jewish friends but many were secular and they ate anything they wanted whenever they wanted. Hal complained bitterly about this.

"Leo and Miriam are Jews by birth and they don't spend a week eating Matzah crackers to commemorate the Exodus of the Jews from Egypt. This is too much, Sian".

"Leo and Miriam are not religious Jews. It is their choice to be secular, as mine is to follow Jewish rituals and laws. Why don't you go to Miriam's and she'll give you a bacon sandwich. There will be no bread in this house until the Passover is finished."

At times I think Hal felt he had been better off with Julia and Lynne where he had had more direct control over situations. But things were changing, especially the role of the independent woman with economic purchasing power. Seductive techniques and feminist stridency belonged to previous generations of women. The new woman had high earning potential and the 'female power dresser' image was promoted by advertisers and image makers of '*the loads of money*' Thatcher era. I was enjoying the benefit of a substantial income since my transfer to the specialist publications for the teaching of Business English for overseas students. From time to time, I had to travel to different areas of the UK for promotions and meetings and occasionally I travelled overseas. The job could be stressful at times but my main issue was being away from home. I always harboured an element of mistrust surrounding Hal and other women. I phoned regularly at different times of day to check where he was. If he phoned me and said he was at home, I'd immediately phone back to check that he was. I shared my obsession and insecurity at Al Anon meetings saying that my husband did not have a good track record for fidelity. We sometimes congregated in a coffee bar after the Al Anon meeting where a member pointed out that I needed to get the balance right between my

Al Anon meetings and spending time with my husband or I could lose him to another woman whilst I was busy sharing about him at Al Anon! Others said something like this: "If you love something let it free. If it is yours it will return to you, if it does not, then it never was yours in the first place." That felt good and took away a lot of my insecurity. Hal had come back to me and we had married. I needed to let go of this crippling jealousy. Regardless of what had happened in Hal's life, the problem was mine, not his. I needed to change *my* attitude. I would never change Hal. One evening Hal showed irritation that I was going out to yet another Al Anon meeting and asked me why I was continuing to go since he was not an alcoholic.

"I agree", I said, "but someone from the group believes you may be a sex addict, so my programme helps me cope with some of the possessive feelings I have for you".

He started laughing at this and asked me to explain. "A sex addict?" he said, "What on earth is a sex addict? Anyway, I'd rather you nurture your possessive feelings for me as they will keep *you in* check."

It certainly was a brave new world for Hal Stanton but he took it all in his stride - but not without a degree of stubbornness and open rebellion at times.

Three years after our split, I ran into Steve one evening after work at Waitrose in the Finchley Road. We were both standing in parallel queues at the checkout and when our eyes met we immediately acknowledged one other. He said I looked 'very good indeed' which pleased me. I must admit, so did he. He was less haggard than when I had known him and he was calmer, his expression less intense. He hastened over to me when I was loading my purchases into the trolley and suggested a quick coffee. I somewhat reluctantly agreed as I knew Hal was working at home that day and it annoyed him if I was home late without telephoning. Hal stipulated that he didn't want to eat after 6.30 p.m. as late meals gave him chronic indigestion in the evening. Personally, I believed he was just hungry but I went along with it. I was apprehensive about the time it took to queue and drive out of the Waitrose carpark, although my home was barely 3 miles away. After we had sat down to our steaming cappuccino in the Waitrose cafe, Steve enthusiastically told me he was working in the Scottish Highlands and he was about to marry his girlfriend of two years. She was single, a primary school teacher who adored hiking and exploring remote parts of Scotland. He was in London briefly to finalise the sale of the lease on his West Hampstead flat. Last year his son had come over from Australia and stayed with him and his girlfriend at his property for three weeks. He regularly attended Alcoholics Anonymous meetings and hadn't had any alcohol since the day he had scarred my face with the glass in his kitchen. He leaned forward across the table at this point and scrutinized my cheek, touching it gently.

"I am so sorry about that, Sian". He looked closely at me: "There's hardly anything there now."

I pulled back sharply; I felt uncomfortable and didn't quite know why. There was a brief awkward silence between us but it was good to see him looking so well and feel his enthusiasm for life.

We exchanged news and updates and I told him about my marriage to Hal. He looked both amazed and slightly shocked.

"Do you still love that man Sian?"

"Steve, Hal is not 'that man'. He is my husband and I love him very much and we are both very happy together."

He looked at me with that familiar sardonic expression of his. "Don't be so defensive. My guess is that you are working full time and… seeing those Waitrose bags, doing the shopping and running the home. His type belongs to the era of the 'Jolly Boy' films with Kenneth More.

"Well, you don't have to worry about it. I know what I've taken on. No relationship is ever perfect – it's about your feelings for someone and what you can adjust to over time". Unlike my relationship with Beni, I did not have too many regrets surrounding my relationship with Steve only that I had allowed it to drift on for too long, partly out of loneliness and partly out of laziness. I had known for years that Steve and I were unlikely to make things work long term as the spark between us just wasn't there, at least on my side. Steve already had a drink problem when he met me which he now acknowledged as we drank our coffee together.

I glanced at my watch restlessly. "Steve, I'm really sorry but I have to go now as it's getting late. It was a fortunate coincidence bumping into you at Waitrose as I now know you are well and happy with a lovely lady with whom you have a lot in common and who appreciates you. It was really great meeting up again and I'm genuinely pleased that things are working out well for you."

Then Steve did something quite unexpected. A moment ago, he had been expounding the virtues of the woman he was about to marry but he instinctively seized my hand and held it, saying in a low voice: "Sian, I think I will always have a soft spot for you. I have always had a lot of feelings for you, do you know that?" My head catapulted into action and a wary inner voice said: "Where are we heading now?"

I leaned over and gave him a brief kiss on the cheek.

"Thanks for the cappuccino - perhaps next time when you are in London I'll be able to meet your wife". I tore out of the coffee bar towards the carpark wondering what on earth had made me say such a stupid thing. But one thing I knew for certain, Steve would never have been right for me as a partner regardless of my love for Hal and the regrettable incidents leading up to our final parting. He was now sober with a more satisfying and meaningful life ahead of him. In spite of his whispered feelings of nostalgia for me, he was so much happier and more stable with Margot than he ever would have been with me.

I arrived home in a flurry realising I was over an hour late and expected to find a questioning and irascible Hal. He was in his office working at his drawing board. His back was to me and he was intent on his work. I put my arms around his waist and kissed him on the back of the neck. He looked round suddenly and saw me. He took off the glasses which he had started to wear for close up work. He smiled and said:

"You are a bit late aren't you? Anyway, I've made a really decent potato salad and set the table for dinner. What did you get from Waitrose?"

Sweet normality reigns, thank God. I felt grateful to be here as I was and at the age I was, without the frustrating struggles and insecurities of youth. Small events in life were becoming very precious to me. Who would want to be twenty-five again? I know I wouldn't.

Chapter 22

Music: *'Dreams'*, The Cranberries (1992)

Julia Stanton continued to be the bane of our lives for the first three years of our marriage. She had re-married a couple of years previously but the marriage was short-lived and she was on her own again. Her ex-husband had also walked off with some of Julia's financial assets from her divorce settlement with Hal. She telephoned frequently because she usually wanted money or sometimes advice and consolation about other matters. Hal was still giving her a voluntary allowance as well as generously contributing to both Elizabeth and Alex's expenses. In addition to this he paid half of Shanna's private school fees, gave Lynne an allowance for Shanna and we bought any extras when she stayed with us.

Julia was in the habit of telephoning before we went out of an evening. This meant a half hour phone call that would make us late and the call would distract Hal from the activity in question. Other times she would ring when we returned home, interrupting what would have been a cosy, pleasant evening. Once, just after we had started to make love, Julia's imperious voice came over the Ansa phone: "Harold I need to speak to you urgently about your son. If you care at all, he has been suspended from the university." Hal immediately got up to talk to her and did not return for forty-five minutes leaving me feeling exasperated and angry. He looked worn with worry on his return to bed. He lay on his back looking up at the ceiling. He relayed that Alex had been suspended and Julia wanted him to come to us and spend some time with Hal so that he could "talk some sense into the boy". What I wanted didn't matter. Julia was contemptuous of me and if I answered the telephone she would say, "Can you put Harold on" as if I were the receptionist. No 'please' or 'thank you'. Once I had inadvertently come across a letter to Hal from Julia. He had become pretty dexterous over the years in the practice of destroying other women's letters but he had left a very recent one from Julia in a stationery drawer that I sometimes used. In this letter, which was a money demanding letter, there was a mention of 'the Welsh trollop', and 'how could you have married her?' I shook with rage but there was nothing I could do. Hal acted very differently with Julia to how he acted with Lynne and me. If I angered him, he did not lose his temper. He was firm and in the end I usually backed down. I was afraid of becoming too attacking as I had sometimes been with both Beni and Steve, as I was unsure how Hal might react. The only time I had won a major argument with him was over our decision not to move out of London. But in hindsight I think this had more to do with the fact that commuting would affect me directly and I was a substantial contributor to the family finances. When Julia spoke, Hal showed deference and was conciliatory. Other times she overwhelmed him leaving him struggling for words. His voice lacked the command he used to me and I assumed it was because when I had met him I was so young and he had continued to treat me in an almost paternal way (my therapist would love this!). Sometimes after a conversation with Julia he would go into his office and bang the door. If I tried to speak to him he would say tersely, "not now Sian, later" and close the door on me.

I shared a lot about Julia Stanton at Al Anon meetings. I found the Al Anon slogan 'live and let live' particularly irritating as I knew Julia would not allow us to live in peace, so how could I just sit back and take it? I detested the woman and dreaded the phone calls. Julia Stanton forced me to experience a feeling I had not had for many years: shame at being who I was.

Alex came to stay with us the following weekend. He was churlish and frequently rude to his father. I felt my blood boil when he sent Hal driving around London one Saturday night looking for a particular kind of takeaway because he would not eat what I had cooked. "Leave it Sian", said Hal abruptly, when I started to complain about Alex's behaviour, "he's going through a bad time at the moment". Alex and I had always got on well until now and I wondered whether Julia was behind his erratic functioning and current bad behaviour. He made derogatory remarks both to his father's face and behind his back. If I heard him say anything when Hal was not present, I would challenge him and tell him not ever to speak like that about his father whilst he was in our house. He would then fall silent and sulk. But overall, the situation got worse. It transpired that Alex was expelled from university for 'smoking cannabis in the dorm', although he protested that all the other students did it and he was the unlucky one who had got caught. Julia had called the Chancellor of the University and goodness knows who else up to the House of Lords but they had refused to reinstate Alex as it wasn't the first time he was caught with drugs. Alex's grades had been slipping drastically over the past year and it was unlikely that he would pass his finals in Economics. I began to fear the worst when I noticed Alex glassy-eyed, demonstrating manic behaviour on occasions. Money had disappeared from my purse and from the bureau where we sometimes kept spare cash for the cleaner and miscellaneous purchases. But I feared telling Hal as he would interpret this as accusatory and labelling of his son. I knew that it would make him angry. He was looking so stressed and care-worn these days that it was the last thing I wanted to do. One day when Alex was out, I searched his room and found some tin foil which I knew from my Al Anon meetings, was used for drug taking. Alex was undoubtedly on stronger drugs than cannabis but if I attempted to talk to him about it he would say defensively, "so you think I'm on drugs then?"

"I don't know. If you are not, fine. If you are, then please tell me, Alex. Perhaps I can help you."

"I doubt it", he sneered, "I very much doubt it".

Alex had no friends anymore and had given up going to the gym and playing rugby, a game he used to love when he was younger. In one of her more colourful conversations with Hal, Julia had sarcastically said that Alex was in the habit of mixing with riffraff and "we all know who he takes after in that sphere." At this point Hal had had enough. He slammed down the phone white-faced. I was shocked at his expression. He was devastated and at the same so overwhelmed with rage that I feared he would have a heart attack.

The final catalyst in our situation happened one evening. I had booked tickets for us to see Delibes' 'Lakme' at the English National Opera. Alex had brusquely refused the invitation to accompany us so Hal and I had agreed to meet directly at the Opera House after work. It was an exceptionally humid day in London. Finishing work early, I impulsively decided to go home before the theatre and have a shower and a change of clothes more befitting to the occasion. I unlocked the flat and went straight to the en suite shower in our bedroom. I was unaware that Alex was at home as the outside door was locked and his stereo silent, a rare treat these days. When I came out of the shower, wrapped in a large bath towel, I was stunned by the sudden appearance of Alex in our bedroom helping himself to money from my purse. I yelled at him, furious and astonished at his boldness.

"Alex, stop! What the hell do you think you are doing?"

He turned around suddenly, shocked at seeing me. I approached and snatched my handbag out of his hands. Noting his trembling hands and bloodshot eyes, I unexpectedly felt a surge of pity towards him.

"Alex, please. Tell me what you are on and perhaps I can help you. I know a number of people whose children attend Narcotics Anonymous and you know I myself attend a Twelve Step Group for relatives of alcoholics. We can get through this as a family if you are at least prepared to be honest and tell me *now* what you are taking."

"Why don't you cut the bullshit and give me some bloody money", he bawled. His eyeballs had shrunk a bare pinprick as he grabbed my bag from me and hurriedly tore the notes out of the purse.

Flustered and uncertain where it was all going, I raised my voice at him: "I'll tell your father about this - just stop it now!"'

"You can tell him what you bloody well like but I'll tell him you lied. There's nothing wrong with me other than what you and him have done to my mother."

His ferocious glance scared me and I took a step backwards, clutching my bath towel tightly around me. He sensed my attempt to retreat and his bloodshot blue eyes stared at me with contempt.

"My mother was right about you. You make the decisions here because you are my father's little tart. You have always been his whore, haven't you?"

"How dare you speak to me like that! You have no right.... I pay many of the bills in this house. Get out of my bedroom!"

I felt my anger rising to boiling point and I experienced difficulty in holding onto a semblance of control; I wanted to physically lash out at him.

He lunged forward suddenly his eyes glazed from drugs. His arm shot out as if from nowhere as he grabbed me, throwing me down hard onto our king-size bed. The towel slipped down revealing my bare breasts. In a split second he was top of me pinning my arms behind me so that I was unable to move.

"Alex", I pleaded, "please let me go. Why are you doing thing this? Why do you hate me so much? Let me go before you do something you will regret!"

"Oh no", he said, "just like my father, I'm partial to whores, especially you. Why do I hate you? Well, my mother knows that when she was carrying me, you and himself were carrying on a nice little dalliance on the side. She nearly miscarried me. Of course, you will lie and say it wasn't true and that you met him years ago at that other tart - that Lynne's house."

I manage to heave him a little way off me whilst fighting to cover myself with the towel. Then something exploded inside my head and I heard myself saying:

"I was pregnant the same time as your mother but I had no choice. *My* child was aborted. The operation was botched so I am unable to have children without very expensive and time-consuming surgery. I have to live with this regret for the rest of my life. My child died as your father intended staying in the marriage. Now get off me Alex!"

He paused for a second, dumbstruck by my disclosure, but when I attempted to heave him off, he gripped me and I felt his lips on mine as he caressed my naked breasts. I hit him in the face with all my strength and he loosened his grip of me. I moved quickly but he caught me before I could roll off the opposite side of the bed. He yelled, "Keep still. You are going to enjoy this, slag as you are."

I started to scream loudly, praying one of the neighbours would hear but then despair dawned when I realised that they would most likely all be out at work. My heart was pumping so loudly I could not bear its constant rhythm and I feared I would die of asphyxiation. I prayed to God in desperation, with the same intensity I had prayed that December evening in Foistneth when I was drowning in the Usk. Alex managed to grab my legs and yank me back onto the bed. He hit me full force across the face leaving me temporarily stunned by the blow.

He positioned himself on top of me and I felt him fumble for the zip of his jeans. I fought like a tiger screaming.

"Let me go, let me go Alex. Don't do this please. Don't do this to your father. You will regret it for the rest of your life. Take the money if that's what you want. Please, let me go!"

Then I heard a familiar voice from nowhere shout "Stop now!" I felt Alex pull away and as he did, he found himself staring into the livid blue eyes of his father.

I can't remember well the sequence of the events that followed but all I know is that they unfolded without affect, flat and in slow motion. Alex's expression was one of stark terror and I was in shock. I sat up hugging the towel around my body. Alex half paused awkwardly, as if he was about to say something

"Get out!"

Hal turned his back on Alex and his voice was cold; devoid of any emotion. He stood gazing out onto the garden.

I got off the bed and went towards Hal but his body posture frightened me. I stopped in the middle of the room and spoke to his back. "Hal, he's off his head with drugs. I don't think he knew half of what he was doing. He's mixed up and Julia…" I trailed off knowing it was pointless.

"It was a good thing then that I too decided to come home early. Tell him to leave my house now. I will have a shower when you are getting ready or we will be late for the opera.

"Oh Hal, we are not going to the opera after this, are we?"

"Why not? Is there any reason why we should change our plans? Are you not up to it?"

Cold, frighteningly unfamiliar, over-controlled voice. I would have preferred a million times to see him angry. I hesitated, but he ignored me. I went to relay his words to Alex who muttered he was already packing his things and about to leave. I had the presence of mind to give him £30 as I knew he did not have any money. He mumbled a thank-you with a bowed head. He was visibly shaking in front of me and the sweat was pouring down his face. I went back to the bedroom to prepare myself cosmetically for the evening. As I was making up my eyes, a terrible fear gripped me and I dropped my eyeliner. What if Hal believed that I had encouraged Alex? How long had he been at the door? How much had he heard? Would Alex try to exonerate himself by telling his father I had seduced him? I knew Hal would never forgive me and our relationship would effectively be over. He changed in silence, we left the flat in silence, without our usual glass of wine before departure. He called a taxi and we drove to the theatre in silence. My worst fears were now confirmed. During the incomparable 'Flower Duet' of 'Lakme,' I could stand it no more and I fought with the rising tide of emotion but lost it to the tears that flooded uncontrollably down my cheeks. I looked at Hal's frozen expression, as if set in marble. I decided to take a risk. I reached over and squeezed his right hand with my left. Within seconds, he squeezed my hand back.

"It's all right darling", he said gently but dispassionately, "I am not angry at you." I watched the rest of the Flower Duet in ecstatic joy and tremendous relief.

We had barely entered the flat after the opera when Julia rang. Hal had gone to the bathroom and I answered the call, believing it might be a call from Pearl but instead Julia barked imperiously:

"Is my husband there?"

"No", I said sharply, "but *my* husband is. Do you want to speak to Hal, Julia?"

She grunted something undistinguishable and I handed Hal the telephone when he entered the living room. I made as if to leave the room, the way I always did when he held conversations with Julia. But this time he motioned me to the telephone and surprisingly put his arm around my shoulders. I could hear Julia's strident voice asking why Alex was so upset and what had the Welsh trollop done to upset him? Hal let her rant and rave. She paused briefly and took - what sounded to me - like a slurp of liquid. "Are you still there Harold?"

Hal answered coldly and very calmly:

"Yes, Julia I am still here but only for a very short time until I have given you some very clear instructions:

"1. Your son has a drug problem and he needs help. Help Him. He tried to rape my wife tonight.

2. Stop feeling sorry for yourself. You are a fortunate woman to have been maintained financially all these years without doing anything in exchange for the money.

3. Get off your backside and find a job to keep yourself. From next month I am stopping all payments to you, Elizabeth and Alex. If Alex rehabilitates himself and returns to university then I am prepared to make some concessionary payment but only whilst he is a student.

4. Never, ever, refer to my wife as 'a Welsh trollop' again or by any other foul name your bitter and twisted mind can conjure up.

5. Never telephone me again. We will be changing our telephone number and all our correspondence will go through solicitors. If you write to me directly, I will return your letters unopened. The children may contact me by letter. Now, goodbye Julia."

Hal then replaced the receiver firmly and looked into my eyes: "I should have done that years ago", he said. He pulled out the telephone line and held me close to him, his chin resting on my head. I felt cradled and safe but totally lost for words.

He said: "Sian, I've treated you very badly. No darling listen, I need to say this. I heard what you said to that silly oaf about your abortion. I never knew that was the reason why you couldn't have children as you never told me. I remember what a naïve but bright child you were then, you practically didn't know which knife to use. You came out of that screwball family of yours and stayed sane. You are this highly desirable, sophisticated woman that has overcome so many difficulties and traumas. How many people in Western civilization have a loved one killed in front of their eyes and are accused of murder? You survived and went onto better things because you are a survivor Sian, a truly great survivor. You are and always have been so loyal to me and I know I don't deserve you. I heard you say, 'it will kill your father' and it really hit me how very protective you are of me, how you put my interests above your own. I am afraid I deserve the Julias and the Lynnes and the shallow superficiality of my own existence. But you have taught me to be less selfish, and not to take good things for granted but to be grateful for many of the positive things around me, something I have always struggled with because I am so very self-centred much of the time. These last three years with you have been the happiest of my life.

I really love you, Sian." He hugged me tightly and I relaxed. I then pulled away and looked into his eyes that were streaming with tears. I was crying too with overwhelming emotion as I had never believed he was capable of such depth of feeling and I leaned my head against his chest. We stood in that same position for unaccountable time, holding each other, and without moving. Round and round in my head swirled the music of Delibes' masterpiece, 'The Flower Duet'.

Chapter 23

Music 'Candle in the Wind', Elton John (1997)

(Ten Years later)

The following ten years brought joy and sorrow, pleasure and pain to the three of us. Anna lost her father to cancer and his passing caused her great sorrow. Anna's parents had approached her after the birth of her older son Daniel. The birth of their first male grandchild had been instrumental in the Kleins' decision to make contact with their daughter again. After a mutually rewarding meeting with Andrew, they decided they wanted regular contact with Anna and her family. Even Juliet liked Andrew and was impressed by the stability of her daughter's life and her compatibility with her husband. Dr Klein insisted that Juliet should stop ruminating: "Andrew is such a nice man. If only he were Jewish."

Dr Klein would have none of it.

"Now we have decided to accept their marriage there is not much point in wanting things to be different or we make only ourselves miserable. Remember Frau Klein, Anna could have married a Jew and been unhappy. Not all Jewish marriages are good marriages. Let us thank God for a man that loves and respects our daughter and makes her happy."

Anna had missed her parents, especially her father, but unbeknown to their parents, her brother Myron and his wife had always been regular visitors to her home. This approach from the Kleins had indeed been long coming but it made Anna ecstatically pleased and grateful. Although Anna and I had had regular telephone contact for some years, we had not been able to see very much of each other. Her two sons were growing up and weekends were taken up with football matches, swimming and Hebrew classes at the Liberal Synagogue in Birmingham. She was also busy with the social activities and fund-raising for Andrew's Church as well as being active on the Council of

Christians and Jews. Anna had a very full life indeed and her visits to the capital were rare these days.

Harry Klein suffered illness from bowel cancer for eight months and for the last three he was bedridden. Anna accepted that his health was not going to improve. She prayed for a quick release for him because he was in so much pain, but when the end came she was not as prepared for it as she believed herself to be. She keenly felt his loss and said she would never have got through it without the love and support of her husband and her closest friends. She was fortunate to be with her father in Cardiff at the time of his passing. He died in the early hours of the morning, the day after she had visited him for the last time. She wept uncontrollably when she was informed of his death. Juliet, Lawrence and Myron took it much better than Anna did.

Juliet Klein now lived alone with Lawrence. Myron and his wife were both lawyers and they had three children, two daughters and a young son. Myron and his family mainly attended their Orthodox Synagogue in North London on the religious festivals and dutifully sent their children to Sunday School to learn Hebrew. They felt they had done their duty in bringing up their children as Jews. Anna was both religious and observant but by the laws of convention, felt obligated to bring her children up as Christians. Such are 'the slings and arrows of outrageous fortune' but rigid rules on this were beginning to bend. By now, Juliet was visiting her daughter regularly and loved to tell astounded Orthodox Jews in Cardiff that her daughter was married to an Anglican Vicar and that they lived in 'the manse' in a very smart area of Birmingham.

We had also been busy. We had moved to a larger flat on the boundary between Swiss Cottage and St. John's Wood. The apartment boasted three spacious bedrooms and a box room. The large reception room lead onto the garden patio, and there were two bathrooms with an entrance cloakroom. The kitchen was farmhouse style with an agar and a terracotta floor. There was a garage for Hal's top of the range Jaguar whilst my modest Vauxhall Corsa remained outside. The flat cost a small fortune but Hal was earning very good money on free-lance contract work and I had a substantial salary. He was adamant that the property would be a good investment. He engaged a firm of professional decorators and I worked with them at choosing colours for the décor and the soft furnishings. I liked wood floors so that the living-room floor and hall were Amtico random plank. Hal chose the fittings for his small office himself as he wanted the best use of space as well as a fresh modern design. I could not believe I was living in such a property and all my friends and colleagues were appropriately surprised and impressed, as none of them came near to owning anything as grand.

Things were going well with Hal's children. Shanna was twenty-one and working temporarily at the London Futures Market as a trader. She had an Honours Degree from London University in Business Studies and was considering going into advertising. She was ostensibly resident in Tunbridge Wells but commuting to work from Swiss Cottage was considerably easier so she had a permanent bedroom with us. Shanna also needed to stay and talk to me after numerous quarrels with her mother, her stepfather, two stepbrothers or her current boyfriend. Both Hal and I continued to spoil her and she could wrap both of us around her little finger.

Hal's daughter eldest child Elizabeth had reluctantly surfaced some months after her allowance was cut. Elizabeth was a research scientist and worked for a pharmaceutical company in Middlesex. I grew to like and respect her as time went on and she showed Hal a great deal of affection. She was gay and lived with a very pretty partner called Melanie. I thought how ironic it was that Hal of all people, should have a 'gay' daughter. He was not happy about it and continued to complain that Elizabeth was mistaken about her sexual identity. I suggested to him the slogan 'live and let live' but this made him more irate - telling me that 'surprisingly for an educated woman', I was 'prone to American brainwashing' and 'to silly slogans of questionable validity.' It took him a long time to accept Elizabeth's sexual choice and even then he nurtured the hope that one day his daughter would become 'normal.' Although Elizabeth and Mel became regular visitors to our home, they never stayed overnight.

And what of Alex? Alex took a year out and then completed his Economics degree. He travelled overseas and worked with the Red Cross in West Africa and when he was in Nairobi, he found some temporary work as a correspondent for a well-known news agency. He then decided he wanted to work permanently as a journalist and was fortunate enough to find employment in this hugely competitive field on his return to the UK. Alex and Hal didn't speak for nearly two years after the incident at our flat. Alex wrote to both of us separately apologising and blaming 'being stoned off my trolley' for his actions. He went to a drugs rehabilitation unit but relapsed twice after discharge. However, he has been drug-free now for four years and is a regular attendee of Narcotics Anonymous meetings. He also saw a cognitive therapist for a year to help him sort out many of the issues surrounding his parents' rocky relationship. He would endlessly quote Philip Larkin's poem beginning: 'They fuck you up your mum and dad' and would recite this aloud to the delight of Shanna and her friends who all responded with timeless giggles to Alex's wit. Elizabeth did not have Alex's sense of humour and was much more serious in her approach to life.

Theodore died suddenly of a stroke in 1994. It was unanticipated that he would leave his inheritance to my mother and myself but that is exactly what he did. It was predictable that the old maxim 'blood is thicker than water' should come through in the end. I always remember my grandmother lamenting to my mother, "but is it thicker than a mattress, that's what I would like to know?" In the end, he left £50 in his will to Mattie the Mattress and £80,000 of his savings and his share of Davy Cottage to me. Davy Cottage carried a substantial price in spite of its lack of facilities and general upkeep because of its situation in National Park land. Housing in the district of Foistneth was at a premium and house prices were on a par with top prices in Cardiff. But Davy Cottage needed work done for it to fetch the highest price as Sir Rob's DIY-type extension, carried out by 'an apprentice builder' of some prior decades, detracted from its value. We travelled to the village near Foistneth in Hal's new Jaguar. I had insisted he bought it as I knew how much he loved top of the range Jaguars. We briefly visited the Glaisfar Hotel where Hal had stayed all those years ago and where our first encounter took place. The Glaisfar been treated to a particular type of urban makeover to appeal to a younger, professional clientele. Tiled floors and 'military barks' had disappeared along with Sir Rob's quarry, salmon fishing rights and tied cottages. My grandfather had been right, Sir Rob had squandered his legacy and had sold off much of the Fenton estate to pay off his debts. Precious few assets survived to be passed onto his son and daughter.

I was surprised that Iris was still working at the Glaisfar. She recognised Hal and made a fuss of him, calling him 'Mr Stanton' but did not recognise me. When I told her who I was her mouth dropped open in amazement.

"Sian Bayley", she gasped, "really, is it you?"

When I told her Hal and I were married, she was unable to hide her obvious shock at the news and I knew she couldn't wait to tell the other members of staff, although I doubted whether any of them knew me. It transpired that someone had spied Hal and I together some years ago and had speculated on it but the incident was forgotten over time. Iris called me 'Mrs Stanton', although I told her to call me 'Sian' - mentioning we had worked as waitresses together. But Iris was 'too proper' to break hotel protocols.

"So that's what a big car and a changed accent does for you", I thought. No wonder I never fitted in here. We decided to stay in a hotel close to Monmouth as Davy Cottage was uncomfortable and smelled of damp. Hal had checked the house for rising damp and suggested certain alterations and a damp course. My mother was adamant that she did not want the inconvenience of builders and workmen on the premises. She became hysterical when I was firm with her so Hal suggested we left it for the time being. I could not help smugly musing as we sped along the M4 motorway on our return to London, that I was now financially the best off of the three of us when previously, I had always been the poorest. I felt that my grandmother was vindicated in a way. I prayed she would know of my good fortune which was all due to her love and tenacity and to the values she and my grandfather had instilled in me as well as to the legacy they had left me.

Pearl and Paul Edgcombe were now married. They had sold their ex-council property at Gospel Oak and moved out of London to Burnham-on-Sea, near Weston Super Mare. Paul had taken up a very senior social work post in Bristol and Pearl had found a full-time post working locally with the Children and Families Team within Social

Services. She was now a fully qualified social worker. But then great tragedy struck. Her son (and my godson) Dylan had become addicted to heroin and crack cocaine. Pearl had experienced years of him living rough, stealing from the family and doing short to medium stretches in prison for drug dealing and shoplifting. Just two years earlier, he and a drug user friend had stolen a car in the early hours of the morning and attempted a getaway through the West End in the direction of the M4 at Hammersmith with the police in full pursuit. Dylan was driving. Just before the Hammersmith flyover, he misjudged the overtaking distance and hit a juggernaut straight on, smashing both the car and himself to smithereens. Miraculously, his friend survived the impact with minor injuries but Dylan was killed instantly.

Dylan's face was so distorted by the accident that they had to reconstruct a model of the face for identification. Paul and I identified him as Pearl was traumatised by shock. We all feared she'd never recover from her grief. She aged almost overnight and her hair fell out in fistfuls. I took time off work and spent days with her at Gospel Oak talking about Dylan. Pearl was racked with guilt about how bad she had been as a mother and if only she had left Kevin before he started hitting the children and causing Dylan psychological problems. I kept telling her it was not her fault. With hindsight we would all do many things in our lives differently but that is *always* with the benefit of hindsight. We did our best at the time with the mental and physical resources or lack of resources we had then. At that time, we thought differently and behaved differently; now our circumstances had changed, we were more mature with less stress and greater understanding. This is the reason why 'lacking' parents sometimes make good grandparents because being one removed from the child, they are less emotionally involved and the experience of years have often made them more aware and more mature in thought and action. Pearl and Paul had tried hard to help Dylan with his drug problem but in spite of their professional understanding and experience, they had been unable to do so. Hal and Julia had been lucky. Alex had stopped Class A drug using before he had destroyed his professional life with disastrous consequences. Many parents are not so fortunate and Pearl was one. I told Pearl that many kids come out of abusive homes but do not use drugs. Others, like Alex, come from affluent backgrounds but they still manage to become addicted to drugs. It is a complex numbers game with many predisposing factors. Pearl listened, cheered up and then moaned desperately like a wounded animal longing to be put out of its misery.

Pearl was heavily sedated by her GP on the day of Dylan's funeral at Hampstead crematorium. The crematorium was packed with family, friends and acquaintances whilst the service was undertaken by a vicar who had never known Dylan. A moving and heart-felt eulogy was read by Dylan's sister, Jennie. Kevin also attended the funeral. He sat at the back of the crematorium with head bowed looking thin and old. I greeted him briefly. He wept into his handkerchief all through the service but left immediately afterwards. Pearl, Paul and Jennie ignored him. Dora had been collected by car from Paddington Station by Paul and she was on true form. She was now well into her eighties but she looked at least ten years younger. Like all of us at the present time, even Dora had stopped smoking after suspected lung cancer. Dean had died of AIDS in the mid1980s and Brenda the Boast had died of a long illness the previous year. Dora now lived alone in her bungalow in Foistneth and showed remarkable resilience in her mature age. She drank large tots of whiskey on a regular basis and went to bingo every Saturday night. Even during the sadness at Dylan's funeral, she managed to ask Hal if he had ever seen a Nippy at Lyons Corner House in the Strand.

Chapter 24

Music: *'When You Walk Through A Storm',* Virtual Choir 300 voices.

Hal and I decided to spend Christmas 1999 in London and not visit Pearl and family as previously planned at Burnham-on-Sea. We had spent the previous New Year there and it had been understandably sad and heavy following the loss of Dylan. This year we had been invited to a client of Hal's who had a palatial residence in St. John's Wood. The client had also invited Elizabeth, Mel and Alex as all three were our guests over New Year. I decided to take the car as taxis were particularly hard to find at New Year and Hal may decide he needed to return home soon after midnight. His physical health was showing some deterioration but he refused to arrange a further appointment with his GP. His indigestion had not improved in spite of medication and he had begun to suffer from the occasional stabbing pain in the chest. He kept telling me that he would have it checked by his GP but so far had not got around to doing it.

The New Year's Eve millennium buffet was lavishly sumptuous. After midnight the food was cleared away and a live band played everything from Frank Sinatra and Whitney Houston to Auld Lang Syne to. We all kissed and hugged each other at midnight and I suddenly remembered New Year in 1980 in Chichester when Hal and I had re-discovered one another and made love along the footpath close to the shore. We both knew then that we were still committed to one another but nevertheless I believed I would never see him again. And here we were in 'almost' the year 2000, married and enjoying the benefits of our close family around us. All except Shanna that is, who had decided stay with her mother this year and go out with her friends in Tunbridge Wells.

Hal enjoyed himself dancing with myself and Mel but suddenly he decided to sit down. He felt a little breathless and asked me to fetch him a glass of water. He looked exhausted and tentatively suggested we went home. We made our goodbyes and as we left the dance floor a spirited Mel, dancing with a man and high from a combination of mixed cocktails and quality wine shouted out: "Why don't you drop Hal off and come back and enjoy yourself, Sian? I'm sure he won't mind. You don't always have to be so self-sacrificing you know. Feminism seems to have passed you by somewhere!"

I mumbled something about Hal not being well but when we got home, he said suddenly:

"Do I take you for granted Sian? I don't mean to."

"Oh, don't take any notice of that silly Mel. She's got her life and I've got mine. I wouldn't want things any differently, believe me. Now, shall we have some tea?"

We went to bed and fell asleep. I was woken suddenly by Hal caressing my body sensuously. I felt him turn me and he pressed his lips onto mine. Half asleep I pulled off my nightshirt and reached for him. We embraced and he proceed to kiss me again and again. He entered me and we began to move in rhythm. He said "come on darling, what is it? You are a bit distracted."

"Hal, are Elizabeth and Alex home yet? I don't want them to hear…"

"They can't hear anything; they are on the floor above. They may still be at the party. Let go Sian, let go."

He made me come first and then he joined me with a long soft moan of pleasure. He lay on top of me for a few minutes breathing heavily. We kissed with great tenderness. Still holding each other, we eventually dozed off to sleep. How unaware I was - because there was no premonition nor any anticipatory foreboding - how unaware I was that this was the last time Hal and I would ever make love.

I awoke suddenly as I heard Hal shouting "Sian, Sian!" He had half raised himself into a sitting position, clutching his chest and moaning with spasms of pain. I dragged myself away from my slumbers and gradually became aware of the terror in his ashen face; his eyes were so wide that they appeared protruding from their sockets. "Doctor", he gasped and clutched his heart. I leaped out of bed and ran up the stairs screaming loudly for Elizabeth and Alex. Elizabeth descended the stairs in her dressing gown, tying the red sash belt neatly as she approached me.

"What's happening, Sian?"

"It's your father. My God! I think he's having a heart attack. Call the ambulance please, now."

Alex appeared on the stairs with a woman peering behind him. I vaguely recognised her as one of the guests from the party. Mel eventually appeared and I went to sit with Hal whilst Elizabeth called the ambulance. It all took so long. Not surprisingly at it was just gone 4 p.m. on January 1st of the new millennium. Hal was still groaning in great pain and the sweat poured off him as I tried stroking his brow and talking soothingly to him. Elizabeth decided that one of us needed to drive him to the Royal Free Hospital as the ambulance was taking too long. I was the only person below the drink-drive limit but I was far too overwrought to drive. Elizabeth insisted that Alex drove as he was totally abstinent from alcohol. Elizabeth was calm in a crisis and her self-assurance and authoritative manner reminded me so much of her father. Whilst they were arguing, car keys in hand, the ambulance arrived. The paramedics attempted to resuscitate Hal and administered an injection. I had thrown on some clothes and insisted they took me in the ambulance with them. They were not keen but I vociferously insisted; the others would follow to the hospital in their car. In the ambulance I silently prayed to God to spare Hal. The paramedics attempted resuscitation again. I held his hand when they allowed me to and saw his pale and strained expression. He did not appear to recognise me. "Darling", I prayed, "please live, please live". Hal was rushed to A&E on arrival and I waited with the others in a kind of daze, hoping they would give us news soon. The A&E was very busy at 4.30 in the morning on the first day of the millennium. I saw the receptionist at the desk arguing with a drunk and a young girl sobbing, cradling her head in her hands. I glanced at these people pondering on how our lives briefly crossed theirs for a moment in time, a fleeting moment of pain and sorrow, which under normal circumstances would hold little significance but now would remain as part of faded recall, etched forever in the memory of time. A voice beckoned us to a private room at the far end of the A&E. I think I knew then. I heard the tired young casualty doctor state flatly after we had taken seats:

"I'm sorry Mrs Stanton but your husband died in the ambulance. He was dead on arrival at the hospital."

I remember hearing Elizabeth's voice as if from a distance:

"Alex, could you call Anna Latimer and Pearl Edgcomb as soon as possible. Sian is going to need them. She needs a lot of support from her family and closest friends. We are Sian's only family."

Elizabeth and I looked at each other with tears streaming down our cheeks. She hugged me as I burst out sobbing wildly:

"Why, why, why? He was only sixty-four years old."

"I don't know, dearest Sian. I wish I did. I really don't know why".

Chapter 25

Music: *'Myfanwy'*, The Treorchy Male Voice Choir. Joseph Parry (1875)

It was two and a half years after Hal's death when we three decided to meet up again for a weekend in the area of Foistneth. Because we now lived in different areas of the country, it was proving difficult to arrange time together due to work schedules and family commitments. Our contact with each other was mainly by telephone or text so Anna suggested we get together and perhaps do a trip down memory lane. Pearl and I agreed but I wished we could have met somewhere other than the village of my childhood.

My mother was alive and still resisting the damp course that Hal had suggested. Surprisingly, she adored Shanna who used to say to me when she was younger - to my mother's malicious delight - "I would have loved to have grown up here, Aunt Sian. It's so beautiful. Tell me, is that Connie's house? Did she really used to attack her husband with a rolling pin when he was drunk? Is that where you used to ride Black Bess without a saddle?"

I regret I could never bridge the gap with my mother and 'live and let live' was only applicable when I was a hundred and eighty miles away.

Anna had lost her brother Lawrence the year after Hal died and her mother had moved into the manse with her and her family. Pearl had lost Dylan in 1993 and I had lost Hal in 2000.

Our meeting evoked humorous memories of past times as well as sadness and a deep sense of loss. To briefly mention in passing, Hal was cremated at the same crematorium as Dylan in Northwest London. I took Hal's ashes home and placed the urn in his office. I did not yet know whether I would remain permanently in London and wherever I was I wanted Hal with me. I commemorated Hal's life by planting a splendid magnolia tree at the crematorium with a bronze plaque with his name and date of death. I put on it 'loved forever'. Hal's children tried to get me to sell the flat saying it was far too large for me, although

Elizabeth and Mel had moved in on a temporary basis and let their jointly owned apartment in Harrow. For many months after Hal's death, Elizabeth and Mel feared I would take my own life. I was depressed and coped badly, but I continued to work part-time as it helped me to distract myself from thoughts of Hal and feelings of guilt for not forcing him to ring his GP when he had early chest pains but however bad my low mood on certain days, I did not seriously think of killing myself. Antidepressants also helped when I was at my worst. Mel teased me affectionately saying that I would be a prime candidate for Indian 'suttee' and she was not far wrong. I knew would never love or marry another man. I had loved Hal all my life since the age of seventeen. Instead of diminishing, our love had grown, though matured and modified with the passing years. Our relationship had been very special.

Hal left me financially well provided for and we had agreed that on my death, half of my estate would be divided between Jennie and Shanna whilst Hal's half would go to Alex and Elizabeth. If I remarried, there were other clauses in the will that didn't bother me at all. I had no intention of re-marrying. Lynne had attended Hal's funeral but Elizabeth refused Julia permission saying it would upset me. Such were Hal's devoted children. Shanna spent a lot of time with me (between boyfriends), and Alex sometimes accompanied by 'the love interest' of the moment, was also a regular visitor. Elizabeth looked and sounded so much like her father; Alex did not but as far as 'tangled webs' with women were concerned, he certainly was a chip off the old block!

I was persuaded to sell the Jaguar, not only because I was unable to reverse it out of the garage without mishap and I knew I would never drive it. I refused to get rid of any of Hal's things. His closet was full of suits, shirts and shoes. The en suite bathroom contained all his shaving gear and various eau-de-cologne bottles. I could not bring myself to remove any of them and grew angry when Shanna and Elizabeth insisted that I clear away some of them. I wanted them there because they gave the illusion that Hal was still around, and he would return soon. Not to feel his presence in the house and have his things around me was unbearable. I hoped I would eventually grow accustomed to my loss but it was so hard, so unbelievably hard. What helped me cope in the end was my religious belief. I had now fully converted to Judaism and attended my Liberal Synagogue in Northwest London regularly. Juliet quipped that the chances were high that I would meet 'a nice Jewish man' who was a divorcee or a widower with his own income and home. I would make him a good wife, she thought. I thought this very amusing coming from Juliet, who had always disapproved of me. How many games life plays with us! Anna was married to a vicar and Juliet was living in a manse. I was now Jewish and was a prospect for the type of British Jew from St. John's Wood that Juliet had wanted for Anna in the early days. Pearl had not been a particularly intuitive mother but had ended up as a social worker currently employed by the Child Protection Services in Bristol. Fate had played tantalising games with all of our destinies, allowing us a glimpse of our individual powerlessness over the people and events in our lives. By manipulating the strings of the marionettes, we had foolishly believed that somehow we were able to control them.

We three booked two nights at a hotel at Hay-on-Wye and on the Saturday morning after our arrival, we travelled on to the district of Foistneth. We visited my mother briefly and also had a passable lunch at The Spinning Knight. I half expected the word 'knight' to be spelled 'Nite' in line with Americanised Euro-speak, but fortunately it was not. We recalled old faces and events as we walked through the village. Here was the field where Black Bess was left to graze freely; this was the garden of the bearded lady where we used to pinch the apples and run from her wrath and the floundering blows of her stick. Ah! The cesspit that Dean fell into causing problems for Pearl. Mattie Boyce's house! She had left the village and was living a few miles away with a new lover, twenty years her junior. I said laughingly that she had gone to America with the generous allowance Theodore had left her, so typical of him! I had increased it to £1,000 as I believed it fair.

There was the River Usk still flowing on, oblivious to the reality that we had long left the village or that we had even existed. We did not meet anyone we knew. The Spinning Knight had changed landlords a few times since I had worked there. They had also extended the public bar which previously was very 'spit and sawdust'. Fitted carpets had been introduced together with bar meals and imitation horse brasses. The stone walls which had stood there for almost two centuries were covered in fake antique artefacts. But the appealing double bay windows had been kept in their original form. We sat in one of them and sipped our dry sherries. The landlord came over to join us. He said there were a lot of newcomers to the village and many of the older generation that we knew had passed away or left the village. He showed a keen interest in our families and where we had lived and gone to school. He didn't know my mother as she rarely left the house these days.

Towards the end of the afternoon, we visited the chapel graveyard where Wilf and my grandparents were buried. We commented on the grim angel that had somehow managed to lose part of one wing as well as a prominent toe. We looked through the cold and empty windows of the vestry that looked dated and unused. Pearl appeared melancholy and distracted by her thoughts. I suddenly remembered she had married Kevin here. We walked down to the River Usk and gazed across the listed eight-arched bridge that caused so much consternation to motorists pulling caravans. It was a splendid, early autumn day, sunny and warm. The trees were beginning to drop their leaves and flecks of pale yellow could be detected among the green. I felt an overwhelming sense of gratitude for my life and was so thankful that I had not thrown myself from the bridge that day when I had learned Hal had abandoned me for his family and left Wales for good. How strange things had turned out - beyond imagination. I would never have had the pleasure of knowing what rich experiences were in store for me if I had killed myself then. My life had been so rewarding and my impulsivity could well have ruined my destiny long before it could be fulfilled. At least, that was how I sentimentally chose to think of it.

"Sian!", Anna beckoned, "let's have a photo on the bridge just like the one my father took those years ago. This camera is automatic so we can set it up and position ourselves and it will take the photo on its own. Come on both. Okay, ready!"

The camera was stubbornly uncooperative but fortunately we met a passing cyclist who agreed to take our photo. We stood in the middle of the quarried stone bridge in 'Anna's arch' with our arms around each other in the same pose of our old photo taken as teenagers. The cyclist clicked the shutter. We thanked him and departed up the hill above the bridge to where we had parked our car. I paused briefly and looked back at the breathtakingly beautiful landscape below me. I remembered a printed maxim that Shanna had found in one of her 'Love Is' cards that were popular when she was a teenager. It suddenly sprang into my mind with great clarity.

'Love's destiny is a succession of good and bad timings'.

Yes, that is exactly what it had been. I had met Hal at the wrong age and perhaps never allowed myself the freedom of loving anyone else with the possible exception of Beni. Yet Hal and I had loved each other for most of our lives and fate had so conspired to throw us together in spite of many contrary events and binding commitments to others. Was there a force of destiny that would be fulfilled in spite of our individual choice of actions?

I voiced my theory on 'good and bad timings' to my friends and they commented on its aptness to all three of our lives. As we walked away, Anna analysing, myself arguing and Pearl remonstrating, the setting sun began to slip down behind the hills to the west, bringing the Table Mountain into sharp focus, casting shadows across the landscape.

THE END

ALSO FROM APS BOOKS

(www.andrewsparke.com)

Davey J Ashfield: *Footsteps On The Teign*
Davey J Ashfield *Contracting With The Devil*
Davey J Ashfield*: A Turkey And One More Easter Egg*
Davey J Ashfield*: Relentless Misery*
Fenella Bass: *Hornbeams*
Fenella Bass:: *Shadows*
Fenella Bass*: Darkness*
HR Beasley*: Nothing Left To Hide*
Lee Benson: *So You Want To Own An Art Gallery*
Lee Benson: *Where's Your Art gallery Now?*
Lee Benson*: Now You're The Artist... Deal With It*
Lee Benson: *No Naked Walls*
TF Byrne *Damage Limitation*
Nargis Darby: *A Different Shade Of Love*
J.W.Darcy *Looking For Luca*
J.W.Darcy: *Ladybird Ladybird*
J.W.Darcy: *Legacy Of Lies*
J.W.Darcy: *Love Lust & Needful Things*
Paul Dickinson: *Franzi The Hero*
Simon Falshaw: *The Stone*
Milton Godfrey: *The Danger Lies In Fear*
Chris Grayling: *A Week Is... A Long Time*
Jean Harvey: *Pandemic*
Michel Henri: *Mister Penny Whistle*
Michel Henri*: The Death Of The Duchess Of Grasmere*
Michel Henri: *Abducted By Faerie*
Laurie Hornsby: *Postcards From The Seaside*
Hugh Lupus *An Extra Knot (Parts I-VI)*
Alison Manning: *World Without Endless Sheep*
Ian Meacheam: *An Inspector Called*
Ian Meacheam: *Time And The Consequences*
Ian Meacheam*: Broad Lines Narrow Margins*
Alex O'Connor: *Time For The Polka Dot*

Mark Peckett: *Joffie's Mark*
Peter Raposo: *dUst*
Peter Raposo: *The Illusion Of Movement*
Peter Raposo: *Second Life*
Peter Raposo: *Pussy Foot*
Peter Raposo: *This Is Not The End*
Peter Raposo: *Talk About Proust*
Peter Raposo: *All Women Are Mortal*
Peter Raposo: *The Sinking City*
Tony Rowland: *Traitor Lodger German Spy*
Tony Saunders: *Publish and Be Dead*
Andrew Sparke: *Abuse Cocaine & Soft Furnishings*
Andrew Sparke*: Copper Trance & Motorways*
Phil Thompson: *Momentary Lapses In Concentration*
Paul C. Walsh: *A Place Between The Mountains*
Paul C. Walsh*: Hallowed Turf*
Martin White*: Life Unfinished*
AJ Woolfenden*: Mystique: A Bitten Past*
Various: *Unshriven*

Printed in Poland
by Amazon Fulfillment
Poland Sp. z o.o., Wrocław
11 October 2023

c302f717-455c-43af-b08c-aa6b900e06e8R01